Absolutely Mad Inventions

COMPILED
FROM THE RECORDS OF
THE UNITED STATES PATENT OFFICE
BY

A. E. BROWN
and **H. A. JEFFCOTT, Jr.**

DOVER PUBLICATIONS, INC.
NEW YORK

Published in Canada by General Publishing Company, Ltd., 30 Lesmill Road, Don Mills, Toronto, Ontario.
Published in the United Kingdom by Constable and Company, Ltd., 10 Orange Street, London WC 2.

This Dover edition, first published in 1970, is an unabridged and unaltered republication of the work originally published by The Viking Press in 1932 under the title *Beware of Imitations!*

Standard Book Number: 486-22596-8
Library of Congress Catalog Card Number: 74-107666

Manufactured in the United States of America
Dover Publications, Inc.
180 Varick Street
New York, N.Y. 10014

Editor's Foreword

A study of the United States Patents reveals many curious and interesting devices from which those herein illustrated have been carefully selected. Space limitations have necessitated abbreviation of the text and, in some cases, of the drawings, but in each case care has been exercised in the selection in order that the patent may be truly and fairly represented. The drawings employed are exact copies of each of the selected illustrations, and those portions of the text which appear are direct quotations from the specifications.

In most instances it has been deemed advisable to append a title of our own in order that the purpose of the patent be quickly grasped, and in considering such patents we urge that the reader refer to the text for a complete understanding.

Should any reader wish more detailed information as to any of these patents, it is suggested that he write to the United States Patent Office at Washington, D. C. By giving the number of the patent and enclosing 50 cents, a complete copy of the original patent may be obtained.

The purpose of this book is not to criticize any patent or hold up to ridicule any inventor. We have no knowledge whatsoever as to whether any of the inventions have been commercial successes or failures. The reader, as we have done, can form an individual conclusion as to what commercial success each patent may have enjoyed. Far be it from us, who are neither inventors nor business men, to say that any of the patents referred to are not valuable inventions. In some instances, it may even be that, due to lack of finances or for some other unknown reason, the inventor has been unable to acquaint the general public with the nature and value of his invention. It is well known that the public has never had the opportunity of availing itself of many a worthy, practical, and helpful invention merely because of complete ignorance of its very existence.

It thus may be that through this little book we may bring to the inventor greater financial remuneration for his efforts and, at the same time, give the public information which will lead to so wide a use of the article as to have tremendous effect on the general mode of living.

Should this book be of exceptional benefit to any inventor or reader for the foregoing reasons, we should more than appreciate receiving letters advising us of that fact. Checks may even be enclosed if the individual feels financially indebted to us for our services.

ALFORD E. BROWN
HARRY A. JEFFCOTT, JR.

CONTENTS

Absolutely Mad Inventions

MEANS AND APPARATUS FOR PROPELLING AND GUIDING BALLOONS.

No. 363,037   Patented May 17, 1887.

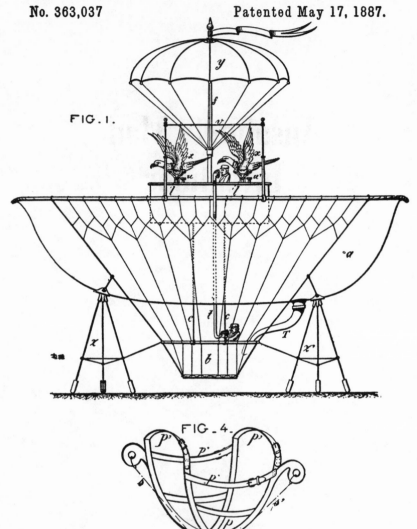

FIG. 1.

FIG. 4.

Balloon Propelled by Eagles or Vultures

UNITED STATES PATENT OFFICE

MEANS AND APPARATUS FOR PROPELLING AND GUIDING BALLOONS

Specification forming part of Letters Patent No. 363,037, dated May 17, 1887
Application filed May 24, 1886. Serial No. 203,078. (No model.) Patented in France, April 21, 1886, No. 175,662

. . . By this present invention the mechanical motor and propelling and guiding arrangements are replaced by a living motor or motors taken from the flying classes of birds—such as, for example, one or more eagles, vultures, condors, &c. By means of suitable arrangements (clearly shown in the annexed drawings) all the qualities and powers given by nature to these most perfect kinds of birds may be completely utilized. . . .

The corsets or harnesses *p* have forms and dimensions appropriate to the bodies of the birds chosen, such as eagles, vultures, condors, &c. . . .

It will now be understood that as the balloon floats in the air the man placed on the floor *d* can easily cause the cross *k k'* to turn by means of the hand-wheel *m,* and, with the cross, the birds *x,* so as to utilize their flight in the direction of the axis of the balloon, or in any other direction he desires. On the other hand, by working the rollers *r r'* he can direct the flight of the birds upward or downward. The result of these arrangements is that the flight of the harnessed birds must produce the motion and direction of the balloon desired by the conductor, whether for going forward or backward, in a right line, to the right or to the left, or for ascending or descending.

It may be observed that the birds have only to fly, the direction of their flight being changed by the conductor quite independently of their own will. . . .

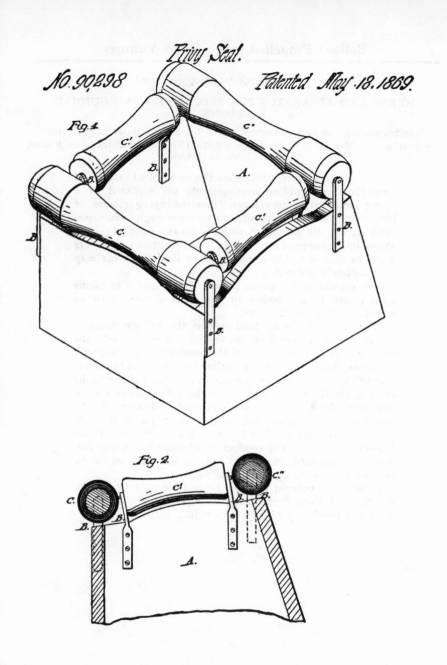

Privy Seat.

No. 90,298   Patented May 18, 1869.

Fig. 1.

Fig. 2.

UNITED STATES PATENT OFFICE

IMPROVEMENT IN PRIVY-SEATS

Letters Patent No. 90,298, dated May 18, 1869

. . . This invention relates to a device which renders it impossible for the user to stand upon the privy-seat; and consists in the provision of rollers on the top of the seat, which, although affording a secure and convenient seat, yet, in the event of an attempt to stand upon them, will revolve, and precipitate the user on to the floor. . . .

A represents the box, having one or more pairs of standards, B, which afford journal-bearing for a roller, C, over the front-edge of the box, and, where necessary, of side rollers C' C' and a back roller, C".

These rollers, while circular in transverse section, may have the represented or any other longitudinal contour, but are preferably somewhat hollowed toward their mid-length, as shown. . . .

EYE PROTECTOR FOR CHICKENS.
APPLICATION FILED DEC. 10, 1902.

NO MODEL.

Fig. 1.

Fig. 2.

UNITED STATES PATENT OFFICE

EYE-PROTECTOR FOR CHICKENS

No. 730,918   Patented June 16, 1903

Specification forming part of Letters Patent No. 730,918, dated June 16, 1903
Application filed December 10, 1902. Serial No. 134,679. (No model.)

. . . This invention relates to eye-protectors, and more particularly to eye-protectors designed for fowls, so that they may be protected from other fowls that might attempt to peck them, a further object of the invention being to provide a construction which may be easily and quickly applied and removed and which will not interfere with the sight of the fowl. . . .

1,175,513.

Patented Mar. 14, 1916.

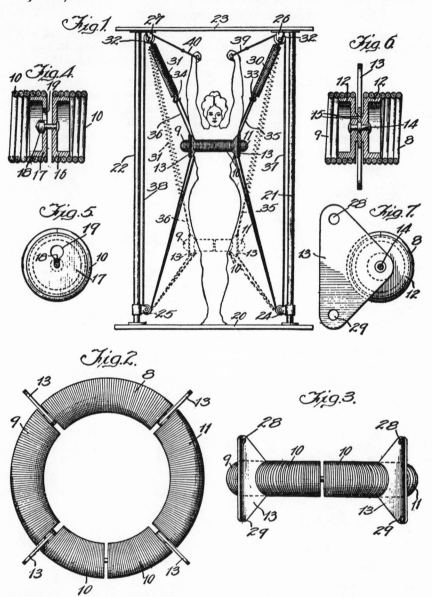

Fig.1.

Fig.4.

Fig.5.

Fig.6.

Fig.7.

Fig.2.

Fig.3.

UNITED STATES PATENT OFFICE

MASSAGE APPARATUS

1,175,518   Specification of Letters Patent   Patented Mar. 14, 1916
              Application filed June 3, 1914. Serial No. 842,556

... The primary object of my invention is to devise a tool which will mechanically simulate the rubbing or kneading action of a hand massage for the purpose of reducing flesh and accomplishing other remedial effects that a well executed manual massage is designed to accomplish.

In addition to the benefits obtained by the use of my improved massage tool, I have devised an apparatus for manually effecting vertical reciprocation of the tool whereby the user is not only benefited by the action of the tool itself, but by the exercise in connection with the operation of the tool as well.

Mechanical massage heretofore has been impracticable for the reason that where a tool has been used, it was almost impossible for the user to apply the tool to all parts of the body. This I accomplish mechanically by constructing a tool adapted to surround the body of the user and which is expansible, whereby the tool will conform to the contour of the body of the user in its reciprocating movement. . . .

The tool member shown in Fig. 2 may be made as large or as small as desired, according to the number of tool units that are coupled together. Where the body is to be massaged enough units are coupled together to surround the body of the user at its smallest circumference, for instance, at the waist. The tool may be opened by disconnecting the caps 16 and 17 so that it may be conveniently fixed in position around the body of the user whereupon the caps 16 and 17 are connected and the user thereupon grasps the handles 39 and 40. By moving the arms downwardly, the tool is pulled down along the body of the user, against the actions of the springs 30 and 31, until it reaches approximately the knees of the user, as shown in the diagrammatic position in Fig. 1.

In passing over the body of the operator, the tool expands or contracts, thereby automatically conforming to the exterior surface of the body, and as each unit comprising the tool is independently rotatable, and furthermore is capable of rotating on its own axis, the action of the tool simulates the rubbing or kneading action of a hand massage by the distorting and twisting action of the individual tool units in their rotating movement over uneven surfaces. . . .

19

RAILROAD TRAIN.

No. 536,360.　　　　　　Patented Mar. 26, 1895.

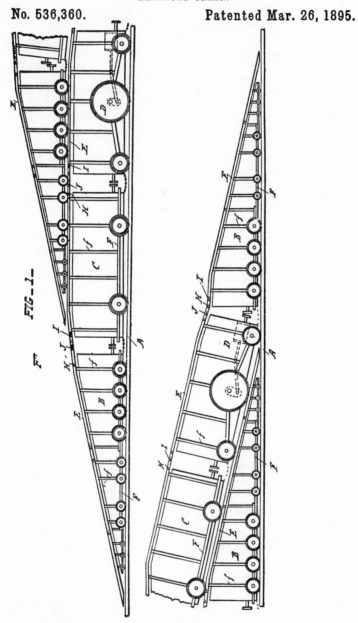

*FIG _ 1_*

Device to Prevent Train Collisions

UNITED STATES PATENT OFFICE

RAILROAD TRAIN

Specification forming part of Letters Patent No. 536,360, dated March 26, 1895
Application filed October 13, 1894. Serial No. 525,824. (No model)

. . . This invention relates to railroad trains; and it consists in the novel construction and combination of the parts hereinafter fully described and claimed, whereby one train may pass over another train which it meets or overtakes upon the same track. . . .

When one train meets or overtakes another train, one train will run up the rails E, carried by the other train, and will run along the rails E and descend onto the rails A at the other end of the lower train, as shown in Fig. 1.

The trains have the inclined lower ends of their rails E adjusted at different distances from the rails A in a prearranged manner so that the ends of the rails E of successive trains are not exactly upon the same level when they meet. The train having the ends of its rails E higher above the rails A than those of the train it meets will rise and run up on the rails E of the other train. . . .

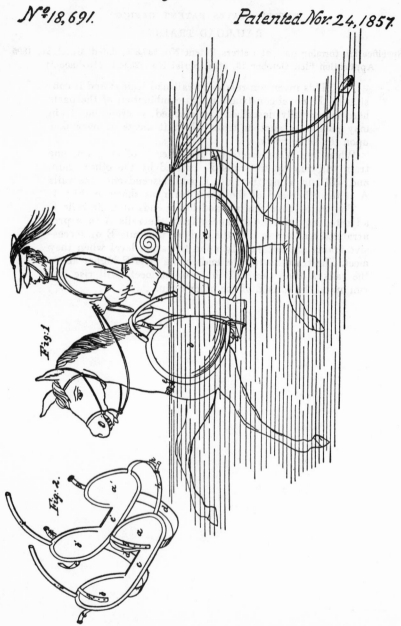

Fig. 1

Fig. 2

Equine Water-Wings

UNITED STATES PATENT OFFICE

IMPROVEMENT IN METHODS OF FLOATING HORSES, &c., ACROSS RIVERS

Specification forming part of Letters Patent No. 18,691, dated November 24, 1857

. . . During a long service on the frontier, where ferries are few, the necessity for some means more portable than boats for crossing the men and animals suggested itself. The want thereof often proves the source of much delay and loss, frequently the delay thus encountered in pursuing Indians being such as to make any further progress useless. Especially has this been experienced on the Pecos, in Texas, the Rio Grande, the Colorado and its tributaries, and on the Columbia and its tributaries. . . .

My floats consist, mainly, of a pair of bags of gutta-percha, india-rubber, or other suitable substance $a\ b\ c$ $a'\ b'\ c'$, each of the peculiar double-lobed form, substantially as represented, the two lobes $a\ b\ a'\ b'$ of each respective bag communicating interiorly by a small duct $c\ c'$. . . . i are tubes through which the bags may be inflated by the breath, the air thus introduced being secured by valves in any approved way. A squadron of cavalry thus equipped, the men having waterproof pantaloons with feet, can cross rivers, lakes, or estuaries dry-shod without the aid of boats. . . .

For emigrants in crossing the continent to California or Oregon, where numerous rivers are met with whose fords are doubtful or far asunder, a few such floats would prevent delay and the serious loss sometimes sustained by using the precarious alternative of rafts. . . .

DEVICE FOR SHAPING THE UPPER LIP

Filed March 25, 1922

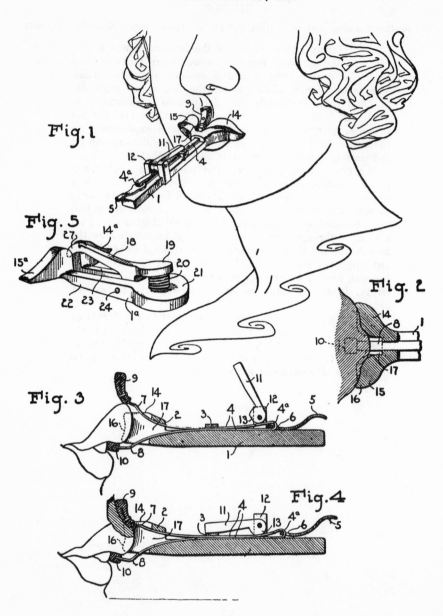

Fig. 1

Fig. 5

Fig. 2

Fig. 3

Fig. 4

UNITED STATES PATENT OFFICE

DEVICE FOR SHAPING THE UPPER LIP

Patented June 10, 1924   1,497,842

Application filed March 25, 1922. Serial No. 546,846

. . . This invention relates to devices for re-shaping the upper lip of a person, and has for its object the provision of a simple and easily applied device to re-shape the upper lip of a person to conform to what is known as the "Cupid's bow," whereby it is unnecessary to resort to a surgical operation to produce this effect. . . .

By my new and improved device, I not only cause a depression to be formed in the upper surface and centrally of the upper lip, but the upper lip will be drawn into shaping relation with the matrix whereby the upper lip will eventually be changed to the form of the wellknown Cupid's bow. . . .

TIME ALARM.
APPLICATION FILED NOV. 16, 1907.

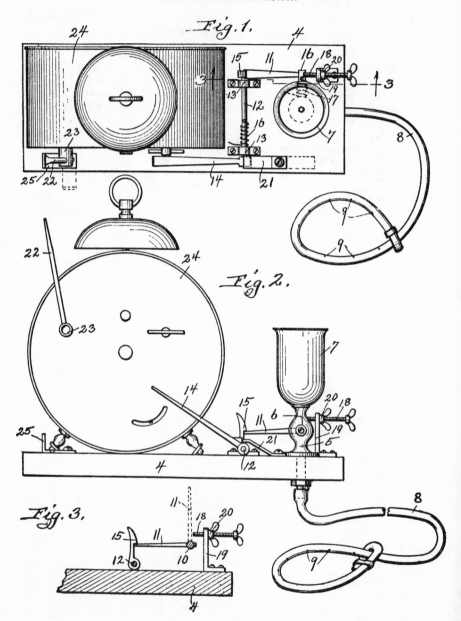

Fig. 1.

Fig. 2.

Fig. 3.

Hydraulic Alarm Clock

UNITED STATES PATENT OFFICE

TIME-ALARM

No. 889,928   Specification of Letters Patent   Patented June 9, 1908
Application filed November 16, 1907. Serial No. 402,550

. . . My invention relates to alarms for waking a person out of sleep, and the objects of my invention are, first, to have an alarm sound at a predetermined time and the action of the alarm to open a valve which will permit water to flow on the person sleeping, second, to provide a perforated hose to direct water to the neck of a person; third to arrange mechanism whereby the alarm can be used alone; fourth, to make a device which will wake any person; fifth, to make a simple, cheap and durable device and other objects to become apparent from the description to follow: . . .

In operation the loop of the hose is placed about the neck of the person; the arm 11 is moved around until its free end is caught and retained by the catch 15; water is placed into the cup 7 and the clock alarm is set for the desired time in the usual manner. At the appointed time the clock alarm will sound, the winding stem turning in a reverse direction, *i. e.* clockwise as view in Fig. 2; the lever 22 will contact with and move the arm 11 a sufficient distance to release the catch 15 from the end of the arm 11; the spring 17 will then turn the valve 6 to an open position and the water from the cup 7 will flow through the hose 8 and out of the perforations 9. The lever 22 after moving the arm 11 will continue in its movement until it comes to stop against the bracket 25 pivotally secured to the board 4. . . .

DEVICE EMPLOYED FOR EXTERMINATING RATS, MICE, AND OTHER ANIMALS.
APPLICATION FILED DEC. 16. 1907.

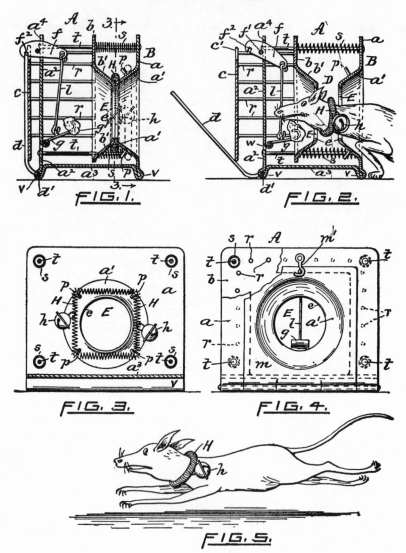

FIG. 1.

FIG. 2.

FIG. 3.

FIG. 4.

FIG. 5.

UNITED STATES PATENT OFFICE

DEVICE EMPLOYED FOR EXTERMINATING RATS, MICE, AND OTHER ANIMALS

No. 883,611   Specification of Letters Patent   Patented March 81, 1908
Application filed December 16, 1907. Serial No. 406,810

... Our invention relates to improved means for exterminating rats, mice, &c., and it consists essentially of a device having a normally closed laterally separable annular frame, an endless flexible resilient band or collar supported by and encircling said annular part of the frame, and spring-resisted tripping means operatively connected with a member of the frame, all constructed and arranged whereby an animal, say a rat, upon introducing its head through the frame opening and seizing the lure or bait attached to said tripping means automatically releases the latter, which action at the same instant also releases and separates the said frame member and frees the expanded band, which latter then immediately contracts around the animal's neck before he can retreat from the device or apparatus. The thus bedecked animal is not caught or confined in any manner whatever but is free to return to its hole and colony. The "bell-rat" as it may be termed, then in seeking its burrow or colony announces his coming by the sounds emitted by the bells, thereby frightening the other rats and causing them to flee, thus practically exterminating them in a sure and economical manner. It may be added that the spring-band or collar is not liable to become accidentally lost or slip from the rat's neck because the adjacent hairs soon become interwoven with the convolutions of the spring to more firmly hold it in place. ...

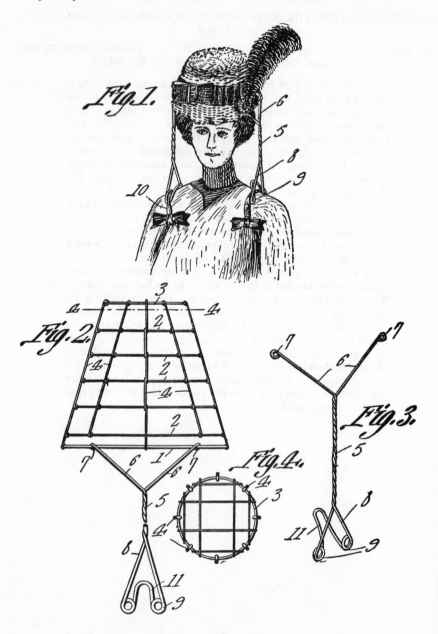

Fig.1.

Fig.2.

Fig.4.

Fig.3.

UNITED STATES PATENT OFFICE

HAT

1,045,060   Specification of Letters Patent   Patented Nov. 19, 1912

Application filed May 10, 1911. Serial No. 626,232

. . . The objects of the invention are, to provide a hat which will permit of free circulation of air entirely around and over the head of the wearer, thus to prevent headaches caused by the weight and close fitting of the ordinary hat; to allow free movements of the head of the wearer independently of the hat; to afford unobstructed exhibition of the ornamentation and trimming of the wearer's hair and of the hat; to remove all weight from the head and transfer it to the shoulders of the user; to render it possible to employ a hat of such size as to avoid the use of a parasol or umbrella, and yet not in any way inconvenience the user by an added weight of material; to adapt a hat to be constructed of any material desired, such, for instance, as waterproof fabric, whereby to extend the range of its usefulness; to construct the article in such manner as to render it at once light, cheap and durable; and in general, to furnish a novel and thoroughly practical article of head-wear. . . .

For storm use, a rubber bag or covering may be employed, which may be placed over the exterior of the hat, or the frame itself may be covered with a waterproof material and thus provide an effective shield against moisture. . . .

1,046,177.

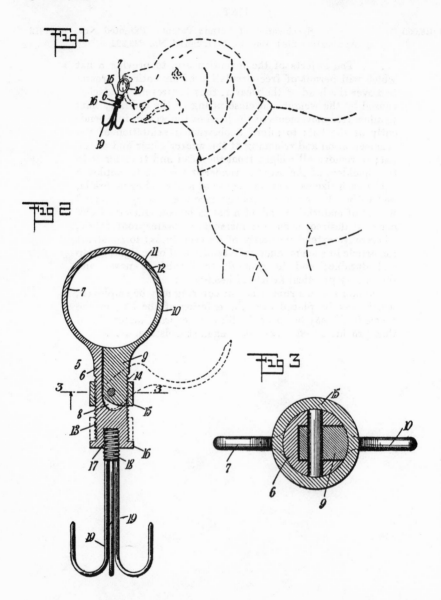

UNITED STATES PATENT OFFICE

DEVICE TO PREVENT DOGS FROM WORRYING SHEEP

1,046,177   Specification of Letters Patent   Patented Dec. 3, 1912
Application filed November 14, 1911. Serial No. 660,248

. . . My invention relates to devices to prevent dogs from worrying sheep, and it has for its object to provide one which may be fastened to the nose of a dog, and which is provided with hooks which will become entangled in the wool of a sheep so that when the sheep starts to run the dog's nose will be pulled, and the dog will receive a lesson which will break him of his habit of worrying sheep. . . .

When the hooks 19, with the stud 18, are secured to the ring member 5, which is attached to the nose of a dog, the hooks will become entangled in the wool of any sheep which the dog may attempt to worry. As soon as the dog is in close enough contact with the sheep to permit the hooks 19 to become entangled in the wool of the sheep, the sheep will start to run, which will yank the ring member 5, and give the dog's nose a severe pull, and, after a few attempts have been made in this way to worry the sheep, it will be found that the dog is very careful not to go too close to the sheep and that the sheep are no longer disturbed at the presence of the dog. . . .

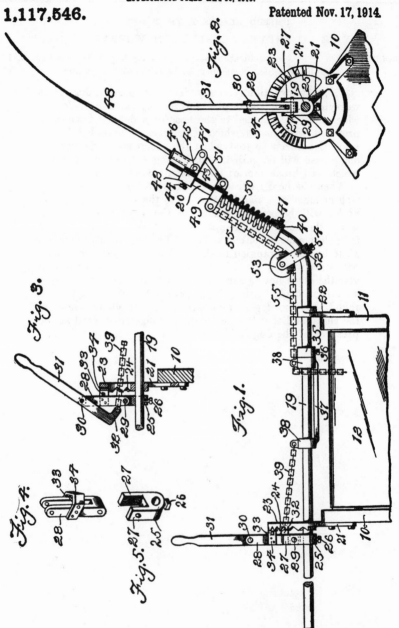

Labor-Saving Whip

UNITED STATES PATENT OFFICE

MECHANICAL WHIP

1,117,546   Specification of Letters Patent   Patented Nov. 17, 1914

Application filed May 16, 1913. Serial No. 768,179

. . . This invention relates to mechanical whips for attachment to a vehicle to enable the driver to apply a whip to any horse in a team, and has for one of its objects to improve the construction and increase the efficiency and utility of devices of this character. . . .

The operator rotates the member 19 until the oblique extension 20 is at the proper angle. He then moves the upper end of the lever 31 forwardly upon its pivot 30 which movement exerts a pulling force upon the flexible member 39 and moves the frame 37—38 longitudinally of the member 19 which movement causes the flexible member 55 to move the sleeve 49 downwardly and thus through its connection by the link 51 with the whip holder 46 moves the whip downwardly and applies it to the horse. When the lever section 31 is released the reaction of the spring 50 restores the whip to its upper position. By this simple arrangement it will be obvious that the driver from his seat can adjust the whip to any desired position and apply the same to any horse of the team, the desired movement being accomplished by the one lever.

When two teams are employed, one in advance of the other, the horizontal section 19 will be adjusted to its farthest point to bring the whip supporting portion opposite the forward team, and then by adjusting the members 19—20 rotatively, as above described, the whip may be applied to either one of the horses of the forward team, the chain 55 being of sufficient length to enable it to be adjusted to correspond to the necessary adjustments of the parts, as will be obvious. By this simple arrangement it will be obvious that the position of the whip is under the complete control of the driver on the seat, and by its use he is enabled to apply the whip to any horse in the team, no matter how many horses may be employed, or no matter how arranged, whether all of the horses are abreast, or arranged with one team ahead of the other. The horizontal section 19 of the device will be increased or decreased in length to correspond to the construction of the vehicle to which it is attached and to correspond to the number of horses employed in connection therewith. . . .

SUSPENDERS.

No. 323,416.

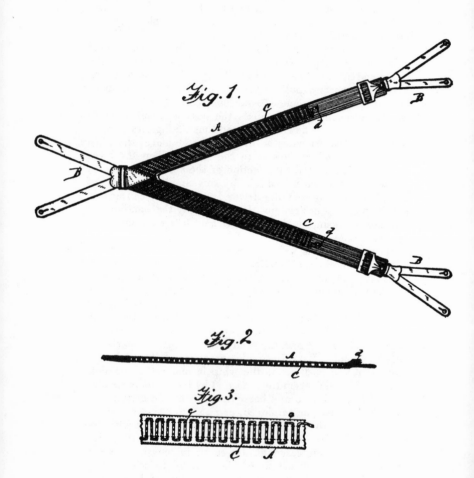

Fig. 1.

Fig. 2

Fig. 3.

UNITED STATES PATENT OFFICE

SUSPENDERS

Specification forming part of Letters Patent No. 323,416, dated August 4, 1885
Application filed February 3, 1885. (No model)

. . . My invention relates to improvements in suspenders, having for its object to provide a suspender with a cord so secured thereto or formed therewith as to constitute a part of the same, and to be readily and easily detached therefrom, whereby, in the event of a person being confined to a burning building and having all of the usual means of escape cut off, the cords can be disengaged from the suspenders and lowered to the ground to receive a rope, and thus enable the person to effect his escape. . . .

ELECTRIC EXTRACTION OF POISONS.

(Application filed Oct. 5, 1896.)

(No Model.)

UNITED STATES PATENT OFFICE

ELECTRIC EXTRACTION OF POISONS

Specification forming part of Letters Patent No. 606,887, dated July 5, 1898
Application filed October 5, 1896. Serial No. 607,955. (No model)

... Be it known that I ... have invented certain new and useful Improvements in the Electrical Extraction of Poisons from the Human Body; and I hereby declare that the accompanying is a full, clear, and exact description of the same, reference being had to the accompanying drawing, in which the figure is a view in perspective of a male subject or patient seated in a chair, the electric battery, and the conducting-wires leading from the electric battery to the positive and negative plates, which in the illustration are shown applied to the back of the neck of the patient and at the same time to the bare feet of the patient or person receiving treatment. . . .

For vegetable poisons I employ a vegetable receiver instead of a mineral or copper one, and for animal poisons I use an animal receiver, such as raw meat, the device being capable of use with the mineral, vegetable, or animal receivers without further change than to equip it with the kind of receiver applicable to the kind of poison desired to be extracted or removed from the human system. . . .

The application of the different receivers is made to the negative electrode, and the positive electrode is applied to any suitable part of the body. When the current is turned on, it will run down from the neck or other suitable place through the patient's body and will pull or draw out the poison at the negative pole and deposit it on the copper plate. From six to eight treatments of a half an hour each in duration will generally extract all of the poison of whatever kind it may be, and the copper plate will show as bright and clear as it was at first. The copper plate or other receiver may be applied to any part of the human body where poison may be found. . . .

Edible Stick-Pin

UNITED STATES PATENT OFFICE

IMPROVEMENT IN BADGES

Specification forming part of Letters Patent No. 174,162, dated February 29, 1876
Application filed January 17, 1876

. . . This invention relates to an improvement in articles of confectionery, the object being to form a badge of confectionery combined with a pin, by which it may be attached to the garment; and it consists in a pin with the badge or article formed from confectionery, cast upon and around the said head, as hereinafter described. . . .

This in no way destroys the confectionery, and may be disposed of in the usual manner for confectionery. . . .

922,956.

Patented May 25, 1909.

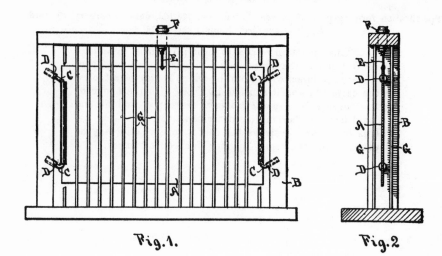

Fig.1.

Fig.2.

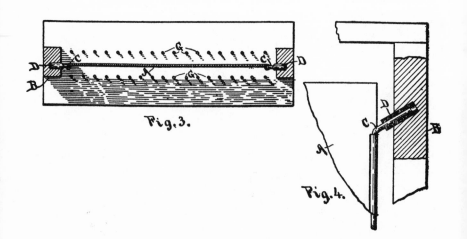

Fig.3.

Fig.4.

Electrical Nuisance Preventer

UNITED STATES PATENT OFFICE

DEVICE FOR PREVENTING DOG NUISANCE

No. 922,956   Specification of Letters Patent   Patented May 25, 1909

Application filed December 26, 1907. Serial No. 408,190

. . . This invention relates to improvements in devices for preventing dogs from committing the nuisance of urinating against buildings, walls, and other structures; and my object is to provide a device which may be conveniently placed at points where such nuisance has been, or is likely to be, committed, whereby an electric shock will be administered to a dog, when attempting to commit such nuisance, which will effectually prevent a recurrence of the act in that locality by the dogs so punished. . . .

The plate, when coupled to an electric light circuit, or to a battery or other source of electric current of suitable power, becomes a terminal from which no current will pass until a ground connection is made. When, therefore, the device has been placed in position in front of a building, or the like, where dogs have been in the habit of committing nuisance, or are likely to commit nuisance, the next dog that attempts the act, will receive a severe shock the instant the stream of urine strikes the plate, by reason of the grounding of the current through the dog's body. After receiving one such shock it is believed that that particular locality will be shunned in the future by every dog so punished. . . .

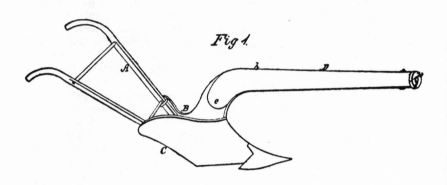

Fig 1.

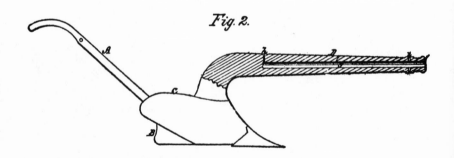

Fig. 2.

Combined Gun and Plowshare

UNITED STATES PATENT OFFICE

IMPROVEMENT IN COMBINED PLOW AND GUN

Specification forming part of Letters Patent No. 35,600, dated June 17, 1862

. . . The object of our invention is to produce a plow equal, if not superior, in point of strength and lightness to that implement as ordinarily made, and at the same time to combine in its construction the elements of light ordnance, so that when the occasion offers it may do valuable service in the capacity of both implements. . . .

It is symmetrical and pleasing to the eye. As a piece of light ordnance its capacity may vary from a projectile of one to three pounds weight without rendering it cumbersome as a plow. Its utility as an implement of the twofold capacity described is unquestionable, especially when used in border localities, subject to savage feuds and guerrilla warfare. As a means of defense in repelling surprises and skirmishing attacks on those engaged in a peaceful avocation it is unrivaled, as it can be immediately brought into action by disengaging the team, and in times of danger may be used in the field, ready charged with its deadly missiles of ball or grape. The share serves to anchor it firmly in the ground and enables it to resist the recoil, while the hand-levers A furnish convenient means of giving it the proper direction.

This combination enables those in agricultural pursuits to have at hand an efficient weapon of defense at a very slight expense in addition to that of a common and indispensable implement, and one that is hardly inferior as regards the means of moving, planting, and directing to that of expensive light ordnance on wheels. . . .

COMBINED GROCER'S PACKAGE, GRATER, SLICER, AND MOUSE AND FLY TRAP.

No. 586,025.   Patented July 6, 1897.

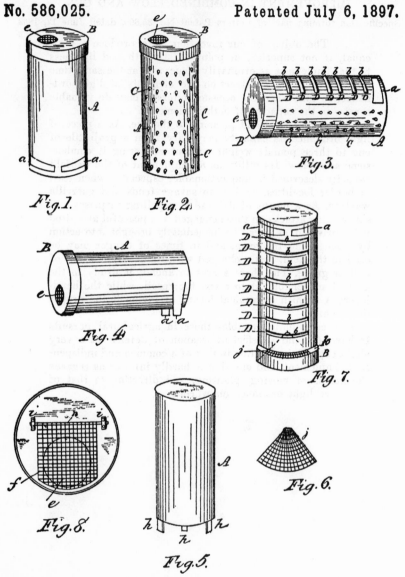

Fig.1.

Fig.2.

Fig.3.

Fig.4.

Fig.7.

Fig.8.

Fig.5.

Fig.6.

Five-in-One Utility Device

UNITED STATES PATENT OFFICE

COMBINED GROCER'S PACKAGE, GRATER, SLICER, AND MOUSE AND FLY TRAP

Specification forming part of Letters Patent No. 586,025, dated July 6, 1897
Application filed January 13, 1897. Serial No. 619,032. (No model)

. . . My invention relates to the construction of a grocer's sheet-metal box in such a manner as to be useful for other purposes, (after the first contents are removed,) such as a grater, shredder, slicer, and mouse and fly trap. I attain these objects by the construction illustrated in the accompanying drawings, in which—

Figure 1 represents a sheet-metal cylindrically-shaped grocer's package or box with feet attached to one end. Fig. 2 represents a similar figure, showing the opposite side constructed as a grater. Fig. 3 represents the same constructed as a slicer. Fig. 4 represents the same as a mouse-trap. Fig. 5 represents the body with vertical feet at one end, preparatory to using it as a fly-trap. Fig. 6 represents the conical wire attachment for the box when used as a fly-trap. Fig. 7 represents the box, the wire-gauze, and box-cover used, complete for a fly-trap. . . .

On the lid B of the box a circular hole e is cut about an inch and a quarter in diameter, and on the inside of the said cover is hinged a wire door f at the top by the upper wire n passing through hinge-plates i i, soldered to the lid, as shown at Fig. 8. The mice will enter the opening e. The wire door f, swinging inward, will enable them to do so, and when they pass it it drops down against the said opening and closes it so effectually as to prevent all egress of the mice.

When the box A is to be used as a fly-trap, a cone-shaped wire diaphragm j, with a hole in the center, as in Fig. 6, is placed at the lid end of the box A when it is laid on a table or other convenient place, three strips of sheet metal h previously being soldered to the mouth of the box A, and when the box is used as a grocer's package they are bent back out of the way, and when used as a fly-trap the said strips are bent outward, projecting from the mouth of the box about half an inch, and when the box is inverted on the cover the said strips form legs, upon which the box stands, leaving an annular space k of about one-quarter of an inch wide between the edge of the box A and its inverted cover B beneath it for the ingress of flies, who enter and crawl up the wire cone through a hole in the apex and are encaged in the upper part of the said box A. . . .

47

Rocking Chair.

No. 92,379.   Patented July 6. 1869.

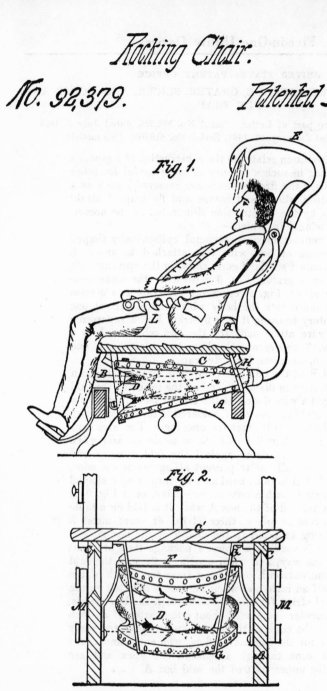

Fig. 1.

Fig. 2.

UNITED STATES PATENT OFFICE

IMPROVED ROCKING-CHAIR

Letters Patent No. 92,379, dated July 6, 1869

The Schedule referred to in these Letters Patent and making part of the same.

. . . This invention relates to improvements in the construction of rocking-chairs, with air-blowing attachments, having for its object to provide a stand or base for the support of a bellows, with tracks or rails, on which the rockers, which are fixed close to the seat, may work, instead of on the floor; also, to provide an arrangement whereby the parts may be readily detached for storage or packing in compact form; and also an improved arrangement of parts, whereby the bellows is operated, all as hereinafter specified. . . .

This stand, with elevated rails, protects the rockers against rocking on small children crawling on the floor, or strings scattered thereon. It also provides for rocking the chair with the same ease, when sitting on the ground; and it also serves as a support for a bellows, D, whereby the occupant may, by the act of rocking, impel a current of air upon himself, through a flexible tube, E, which may be directed to any part, as required.

The top of this bellows is connected by a bent bar, F, to the stand A, so as to be held in a fixed position, while the lower part is connected by a similar bent bar, G, to the bottom of the chair, so as to be moved up and down with it, to impel the air. . . .

CHEWING GUM LOCKET.

No. 395,515.

Patented Jan. 1, 1889

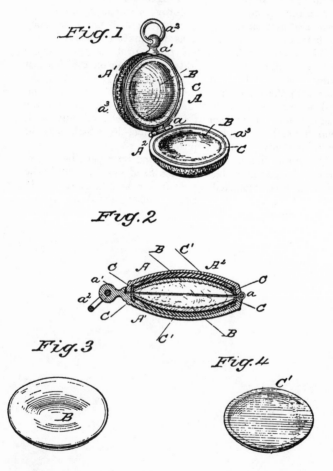

Fig. 1

Fig. 2

Fig. 3

Fig. 4

UNITED STATES PATENT OFFICE

CHEWING-GUM LOCKET

Specification forming part of Letters Patent No. 395,515, dated January 1, 1889
Application filed September 10, 1887. Serial No. 249,394. (No model)

. . . The object of my invention is to provide a locket of novel form and construction for holding with safety, cleanliness, and convenience for use chewing-gum, confections, or medicines, and which may be carried in the pocket or otherwise attached to the person, as lockets are ordinarily worn; and the improvement consists, essentially, in a locket having an anti-corrosive lining, and it also consists in certain details of construction and combinations of parts, hereinafter particularly described, and designated in the claims. . . .

As the lining B is made of a non-corrosive material, any of which may be employed without departing from my invention, the saliva of the mouth or other substance held within the locket will not act upon it chemically, and a case of any preferred material may thus be used. Chewing-gum may thus be carried conveniently upon the person, and is not left around carelessly to become dirty or to fall in the hands of persons to whom it does not belong, and be used by ulcerous or diseased mouths, by which infection would be communicated by subsequent use to the owner. . . .

ILLUMINATING DEVICE FOR FRIGHTENING RATS AND MICE.

No. 305,102.   Patented Sept. 16, 1884.

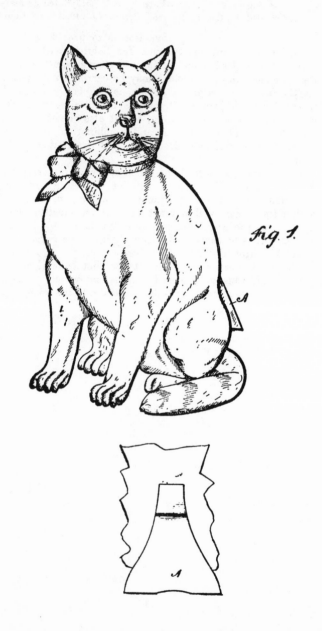

Fig. 1.

Ornamental Rat Exterminator

UNITED STATES PATENT OFFICE

ILLUMINATING DEVICE FOR FRIGHTENING RATS AND MICE

Specification forming part of Letters Patent No. 305,102, dated September 16, 1884
Application filed July 30, 1884. (No model)

. . . This invention relates to a new, useful, and ornamental illuminated device for frightening and exterminating rats and mice; and it has for its object to provide an article of this character which will be arranged and adapted to effect the purposes stated without the use of deadly poisons.

To this end the said invention consists in printing the figure of a cat on card-board having several coats of illuminating-paint arranged so that the figure will shine in the dark; and, furthermore, in perfuming said figure with peppermint, which is obnoxious to rats, and mice, and thus the device will have the effect to drive away these rodents. . . .

Referring to the drawings, it will be seen that I have shown the figure of a cat cut out of card-board and painted to present an attractive appearance, the cat being shown in a sitting posture, with its head turned toward the right and its eyes directed toward and watching an object near by. Over this painted figure I apply several coats of illuminating-paint, so that it will shine in the dark, and then I perfume the figure with oil of peppermint, which is obnoxious to rats and mice, and will serve as an exterminator. The eyes of the cat are coated with a thick coat of phosphorus, so as to shine out with more brilliance than the body of the figure. To the back of the figure is attached a swinging flap, A, arranged to be folded flat against the back or swung outward to rest on the stand or floor, so as to support the figure in an upright position. . . .

As a parlor-ornament the device serves two functions, since it will frighten away rats and mice, and forms a useful and attractive article to place on the mantel-piece or stand. It is also useful to place on the window-sill facing the window, so as to shine through the same and be seen in the dark. It can also be placed in the pantry, on the shelves or floor adjacent to the rat-hole, or near the parts traversed by the rats or mice, and by the peculiar but not offensive odor with which the figure is permeated it will act as an effectual exterminator. . . .

1,159,804.

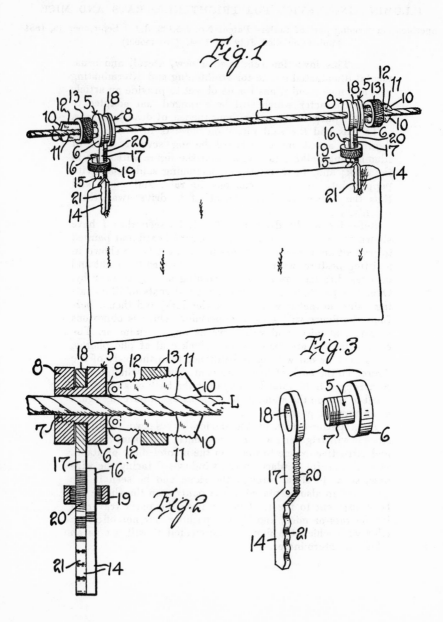

Fig.1

Fig.2

Fig.3

Mechanical Clothes-Pin

UNITED STATES PATENT OFFICE

CLOTHES-PIN

1,159,804   Specification of Letters Patent   Patented Nov. 9, 1915
Application filed May 19, 1915. Serial No. 29,141

. . . This invention relates to an improved clothes pin or fastener and has for its primary object to provide a very simple device of this character which will serve to securely hold the articles upon the line and yet permit of their swinging or swaying movement with respect thereto when blown by high winds. . . .

In the use of my invention, the line indicated at L is passed through the central bore or opening of the body member 5, the eye 18 of the clothes fastener being engaged upon said body against one side of the flange 5. It will be understood that the nut 13 is threaded inwardly upon the dogs 10 so that said dogs may be spaced sufficiently to permit of the free sliding movement of the clamp upon the line. The ring 8 is threaded upon the end 7 of the clamp body and the several parts are then moved to the desired position upon the clothes line. The nut 13 is now threaded outwardly upon the wider ends of the dogs 10 so that said dogs will be forced inwardly and their toothed faces 11 caused to securely grip on opposite sides of the line L. The article is now disposed between the jaws 14 and the nut 19 threaded upwardly upon the shanks 16 and 17 of said jaws so as to force the jaws to closed position into clamping engagement with the article. It will be understood that two or more of the fasteners are employed for hanging sheets or other large articles upon the line. As the fastening devices may freely swing with respect to the line clamps, owing to the loose engagement of the terminal eyes 18 of the clamps, it will be manifest that the articles will not be blown from the fasteners by high winds but will readily sway or swing with respect to the line. . . .

Fig. 1,

Fig. 2,

UNITED STATES PATENT OFFICE

TAPEWORM-TRAP

Specification of Letters Patent No. 11,942, dated November 14, 1854

. . . The object of my invention is to effect the removal of worms from the system, without employing medicines, and thereby causing much injury.

My invention consists in a trap which is baited, attached to a string, and swallowed by the patient after a fast of suitable duration to make the worm hungry. The worm seizes the bait, and its head is caught in the trap, which is then withdrawn from the patient's stomach by the string which has been left hanging from the mouth, dragging after it the whole length of the worm. . . .

The trap is baited by taking off the cover b, of the exterior box, and filling the interior box with the bait which may consist of any nutritious substance. The interior box d, is then pushed down until the stud f, catches between the teeth of the opening e, and holds it with the openings, e, and c, opposite each other, the points of the teeth being then below the lower edge of the opening c. The trap, having the cord h, attached to a ring i, on the lid is then swallowed. The worm, in inserting its head at the opening e, and eating the bait, will so far disturb the inner box as to work it free of the stud f, when the box will be forced upward by the spring g, and the worm caught behind the head, between the serrated lower edge of the opening in the interior box, and the upper edge of the opening in the exterior box. The trap and the worm may then be drawn from the stomach, by the cord h. . . .

DEVICE FOR PREVENTING HENS FROM SETTING.

No. 582,320. Patented May 11, 1897.

UNITED STATES PATENT OFFICE

DEVICE FOR PREVENTING HENS FROM SETTING

Specification forming part of Letters Patent No. 582,320, dated May 11, 1897
Application filed October 15, 1896. Serial No. 608,953. (No model)

. . . This invention relates to improvements in devices for preventing hens from setting; and it consists of certain novel constructions, combinations, and arrangements of parts, all of which will be hereinafter more fully set forth and claimed.

In the accompanying drawings, forming part of this specification, Figure 1 represents a side elevation of a hen with my invention applied thereto. Fig. 2 represents an enlarged front elevation of my device, and Fig. 3 represents an enlarged rear elevation of the same. . . .

When this device is to be applied to a hen, the hood is slipped over her head with the comb projecting through the comb-slot and the bill through the bill-aperture. The strip b^4 is then buckled through the buckle b^3 and the hood thus secured firmly in position.

When a hen is provided with one of these improved hoods, she can neither see to the right nor the left nor upward, and she is thus prevented from flying to any elevated position.

All nests in the modern construction of henneries are constructed at an elevation from the ground, and as a fowl will never fly in a direction in which it cannot first look the hen will thus be prevented from flying up into the nest.

The device will also prevent fowls from flying over fences and into gardens and the like. When a hen is provided with one of these hoods, the action of eating is not interfered with at all, as she can look downward and toward the ground as readily as she could were the hood not in position at all.

It will be observed that while the hen is prevented from reaching the nest or flying over fences she is perfectly free to scratch about or eat at pleasure. . . .

SIPHON SPOUT.

(Application filed Nov. 10, 1899.)

(No Model.)

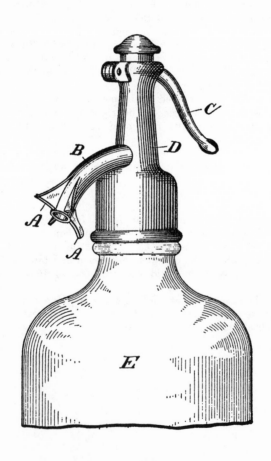

Hygienic Siphon

UNITED STATES PATENT OFFICE

SIPHON-SPOUT

Specification forming part of Letters Patent No. 641,201, dated January 9, 1900
Application filed November 10, 1899. Serial No. 736,565. (No model)

. . . My invention relates to projections on the mouth of the spout or nozzle of siphons; and the object of my improvement is to prevent the use of the siphon as a syringe by inserting it in or applying it to certain parts of the human body. I attain this object by the mechanism illustrated in the accompanying drawing, in which the diagram is a side view of the siphon. . . .

In using the siphon before my invention nothing prevented the insertion of the siphon-mouth in any opening of the body to be used as a syringe, thereby contaminating it with germs of disease. With my improvement in using the siphon as a siphon the projections *a* in no way interfere; but if it is attempted to misuse the siphon—*e. g.*, as a syringe—the projections *a* prevent an insertion in or application to any part of the body. . . .

Fig. I

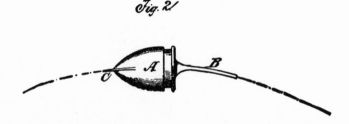

Fig. 2.

UNITED STATES PATENT OFFICE

IMPROVEMENT IN PROJECTILES

Letters Patent No. 107,909, dated October 4, 1870
The Schedule referred to in these Letters Patent and making part of the same.

. . . My invention has for its object to furnish an improvement in balls and other projectiles, by means of which the ball or other projectile may be fired in curved lines with the same accuracy as in straight lines; and

It consists in constructing the ball with a curved flat piece upon its base, whether used with or without a curved flat point. . . .

ATTACHMENT FOR LOCOMOTIVES.

No. 292,504. Patented Jan. 29, 1884.

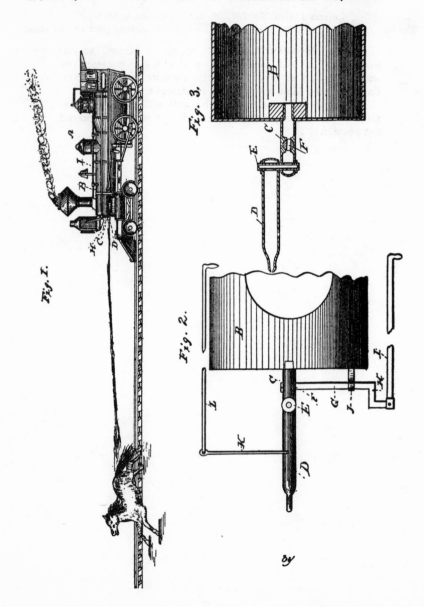

Device for Driving Cattle from Tracks

UNITED STATES PATENT OFFICE

ATTACHMENT FOR LOCOMOTIVES

Specification forming part of Letters Patent No. 292,504, dated January 29, 1884
Application filed March 26, 1883. (No model)

. . . This invention relates to an attachment for locomotives, to be used for frightening horses and cattle off the track. . . .

By means of the rod I the stop-cock F may be opened, thus permitting the water to escape from the boiler through the nozzle D, through which it is driven, by the steam-pressure in the boiler, with a great degree of force, and to a considerable distance, so that it may be employed for frightening horses and cattle off the track. By means of the rod L the nozzle may be adjusted so as to throw the stream of water in other than a straight line, so that the device may be advantageously used on curves. . . .

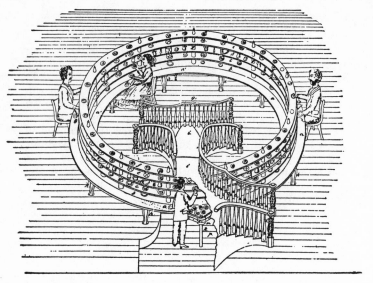

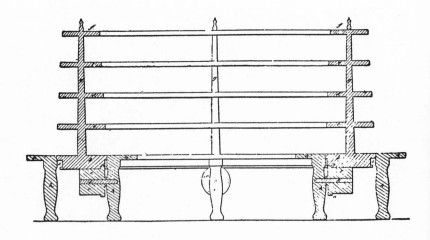

Self-Service Table

UNITED STATES PATENT OFFICE

IMPROVED SERVING-TABLE

Specification forming part of Letters Patent No. 55,677, dated June 19, 1866

. . . The nature of my improvement consists in providing a revolving or moving serving-table, *b*, driven by steam or other power, with either two or three rings or continuous tables, *a a*, for dining and other uses . . . the outer ring *a* and inner ring *a* fixed or stationary, having an open space, on the inside of the table *a*, for the seating of guests, as well as upon the outside of the table *a*, with an entrance or passage-way either above or below the tables *a a* and *b*, the middle or center ring *b* or continuous table *b*, with one or more shelves, *c d e f*, or a succession of shelves one above another, to revolve or move within or between the stationary rings or continuous tables *a a*, and so arranged as to seat persons conveniently at either the inner or outer rings or stationary tables *a a*, the central revolving or moving table *b*, with shelves *c d e f*, arranged one above another, loaded with the entire bill of fare once in every fifteen or twenty feet or sections of the table *b*, and the table *b*, with shelves *c d e f*, so loaded with viands, to move at the rate of fifteen or twenty feet per minute, or to pass before each guest at such speed as to exhibit before each guest the entire bill of fare once per minute. . . .

All persons at this table are put upon an equality and free to act for themselves, and these shelves so arranged as not only to contain the full bill of fare, and that kept hot by lamp or otherwise, but also to contain all the necessary dishes, knives, forks, spoons, glasses, &c., and also so arranged as to carry the dishes that have been used off into the pantry P, behind the screen, where they are removed by the servant stationed at that point for that purpose, and where also are the persons stationed to supply and replenish the revolving or moving table *b*, with shelves *c d e f*. The carver and his assistants are also stationed behind the screen, which we here term "pantry," P, to supply continually the revolving or moving table *b* and shelves *c d e f*. The dishes, after the guest has finished with them, are put upon the lower shelf or table *b*, which is hid from view by means of a lid or curtain.

All the servants that we require in the use of this moving-table is one upon the outside and one upon the inside, except those required in the pantry to put away the last dishes of each guest and brush off the crumbs and adjust the chair. This would be the requirements of a table that would seat, say, one hundred and fifty persons. . . .

DEVICE FOR WAKING PERSONS FROM SLEEP.

No. 256,265.   Patented Apr. 11, 1882.

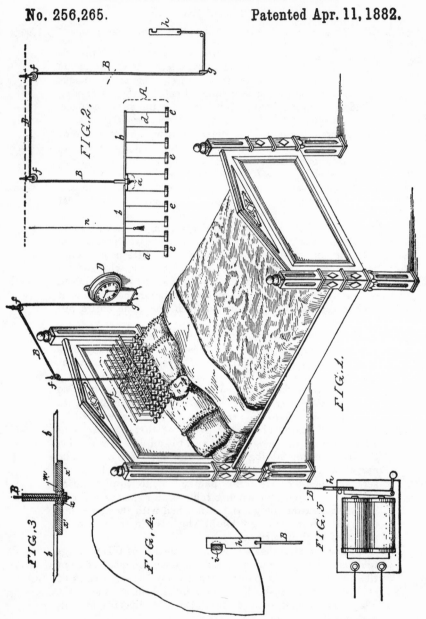

UNITED STATES PATENT OFFICE

DEVICE FOR WAKING PERSONS FROM SLEEP

Specification forming part of Letters Patent No. 256,265, dated April 11, 1882
Application filed December 14, 1881. (No model)

. . . The object of my invention is to construct a simple and effective device for waking persons from sleep at any time which may have previously been determined upon, the device being also adapted for use in connection with an electric or other burglar-alarm apparatus, in place of the usual gong-alarms. . . .

Ordinary bell or rattle alarms are not at all times effective for their intended purpose, as a person in time becomes so accustomed to the noise that sleep is not disturbed when the alarm is sounded.

The main aim of my invention is to provide a device which will not be liable to this objection.

In carrying out my invention I suspend a light frame in such a position that it will hang directly over the head of the sleeper, the suspending-cord being combined with automatic releasing devices, whereby the frame is at the proper time permitted to fall into the sleeper's face.

In the drawings, A represents the frame, which consists of a central bar, *a,* having on each side a number of projecting arms, *b,* the whole being made as light as is consistent with proper strength. From each of the arms *b* hang a number of cords, *d,* and to the lower end of each of these cords is secured a small block, *e,* of light wood, preferably cork . . . the only necessity to be observed in constructing the frame being that when it falls it will strike a light blow, sufficient to awaken the sleeper, but not heavy enough to cause pain. . . .

DEVICE FOR PRODUCING DIMPLES.

No. 560,351.   Patented May 19, 1896.

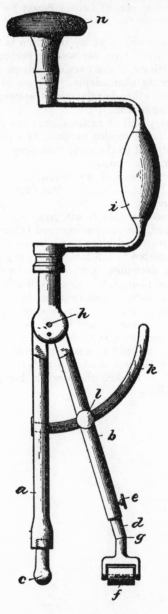

Dimple Tool

UNITED STATES PATENT OFFICE

DEVICE FOR PRODUCING DIMPLES

Specification forming part of Letters Patent No. 560,351, dated May 19, 1896
Application filed May 25, 1895. Serial No. 550,658. (No model)

. . . The present invention consists of a device which serves either to produce dimples on the human body or to nurture and maintain dimples already existing.

In order to make the body susceptible to the production of artistic dimples, it is necessary, as has been proved by numerous experiments, that the cellular tissues surrounding the spot where the dimple is to be produced should be made susceptible to its production by means of massage. This condition is fulfilled by the present process as well as by the apparatus by which the process is worked, and which is represented in an enlarged form in the accompanying drawing. . . .

When it is desired to use the device for the production of dimples, the knob or pearl c of the arm a must be set on the selected spot on the body, the extension d, together with the cylinder f, put in position, then while holding the knob n with one hand the brace i must be made to revolve on the axis x. The cylinder f serves to mass and make the skin surrounding the spot where the dimple is to be produced malleable. . . .

ANIMAL TRAP.

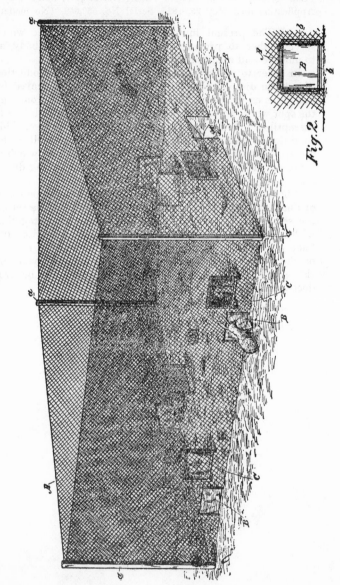

Fig.1.

Fig.2.

UNITED STATES PATENT OFFICE

ANIMAL-TRAP

Specification forming part of Letters Patent No. 383,700, dated May 29, 1888
Application filed February 16, 1888. Serial No. 264,231. (No model)

. . . The object of my invention is to provide an effective trap for rabbits, and one which is at the same time cheap in construction and readily transportable. . . .

Any suitable enticing material or food may be placed within the cage. The rabbit, endeavoring to gain admission to the cage, soon sees what he deems an unguarded opening, the door B being of glass, and therefore not noticed by him. He therefore makes for the opening, and the door, swinging inwardly, does not impede him, and under his original impulse he passes through into the cage. He cannot get out again, for the doors B do not swing outwardly.

Now, in order to better insure the entrance of the rabbit, I place within the cage and just behind each door B a mirror, C, the location being such that upon discovering and approaching the supposed opening of the door B the rabbit cannot fail to observe his image in the mirror. Surprised by this he pricks up his ears, and, his image doing likewise, he is the more impelled to enter the cage, in order to make the acquaintance of so close a companion, for though other rabbits might really be within and in sight, still the proximity and sympathetic actions of the reflected rabbit do more to create a sudden impulse toward the door B than the confined real rabbits do. . . .

Combination Cravat and Watch-Guard

UNITED STATES PATENT OFFICE

IMPROVED NECK-TIE AND WATCH-GUARD COMBINED

Letters Patent No. 79,063, dated June 23, 1868

The Schedule referred to in these Letters Patent and making part of the same.

. . . My invention has for its object to combine a neck-tie and watch-guard with each other, so as to furnish a neat, convenient, and serviceable article; and it consists in combining a neck-tie and watch-guard in one article, as hereinafter more fully described. . . .

In using the article, the middle part, a^1, is passed around the neck of the wearer, and the knot or bow a^3 slipped up to its place. The elastic loop a^4 is then passed over the front button of the shirt-neck band, to keep the said knot from slipping down out of place. The guard-ring of the watch may then be attached to the extreme ends of the neck-tie A by a snap-ring or other means, or the watch may be permanently attached to said ends. . . .

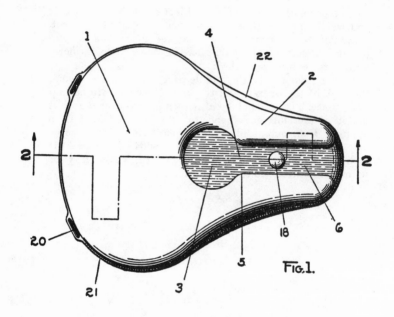

Fig.1.

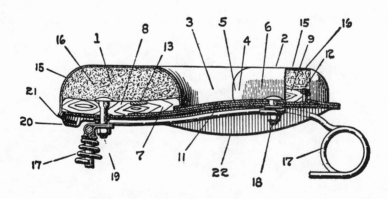

Fig.2.

Bicycle Saddle for the Use of Either Sex

UNITED STATES PATENT OFFICE

BICYCLE AND MOTOR-CYCLE SEAT

Patented May 19, 1925   1,538,542

Application filed February 16, 1924. Serial No. 693,327

. . . It is a primary object of my invention to provide a bicycle or motorcycle saddle having a suitable cavity properly located to allow comfortable clearance for the private organs of the male rider, said saddle having also a channel adapted to allow clearance for the female rider's private organs, to prevent pressure at the opening of said organs due to the weight of the rider, and tending also to keep said organs in a naturally closed state, the sides of said channel being substantially parallel and bell-mouthed. . . .

Referring to Fig. 1, a somewhat circular cavity 3 is formed on a medial line of the apparatus as a whole, at the junctions of said extension with said larger seating portion. Said cavity is of suitable size, shape and location to comfortably receive the private organs of a male rider and more particularly the testicle region of such rider. Said opening is of bell-mouthed formation, the bell-mouth character thereof being formed on the upper portion of said opening. Such bell-mouthed formation is particularly useful to the comfort of the male rider both during the riding act and also during the mounting or dismounting acts, said organs being slidably lodgeable or dislodgeable in relation to said opening when same is thus covered or uncovered by angular movement as compared to what may be called a vertical straight-away movement. . . .

1,278,217.

Patented Sept. 10, 1918.

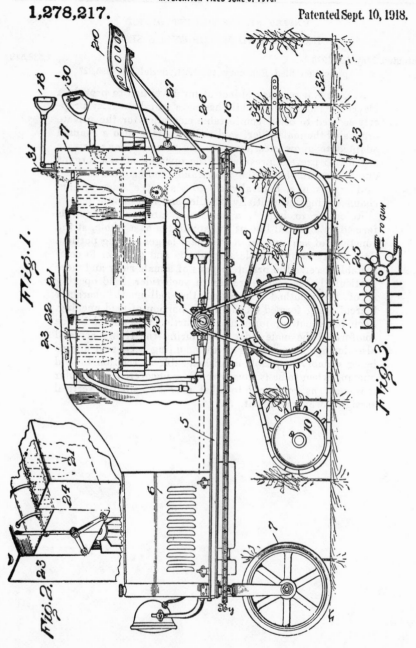

Fig. 1.

Fig. 2.

Fig. 3.

TO GUN

UNITED STATES PATENT OFFICE

APPARATUS FOR IRRIGATING PLANTS

1,278,217   Specification of Letters Patent   Patented Sept. 10, 1918
Application filed June 8, 1918. Serial No. 238,863

. . . This invention relates to irrigating apparatus and more particularly to an apparatus especially adapted for irrigating growing trees and plants of all kinds in climates where surface irrigation, due to extremely high temperatures and dry atmospheres, is impracticable for obtaining the best results. . . .

In operation, the machine travels along between or straddling the rows of plants under its own power and as the plants are reached the gun 26 is fired to discharge a projectile of ice into the ground at the roots of the plant, as shown. The apparatus is of such size as to provide twenty or thirty projectiles at once to the endless belt 25 and while these are being used, a second charge will have been made by the refrigerant in the freezing tank. When not used for the above purpose the apparatus may be used wherever a tractor is applicable. . . .

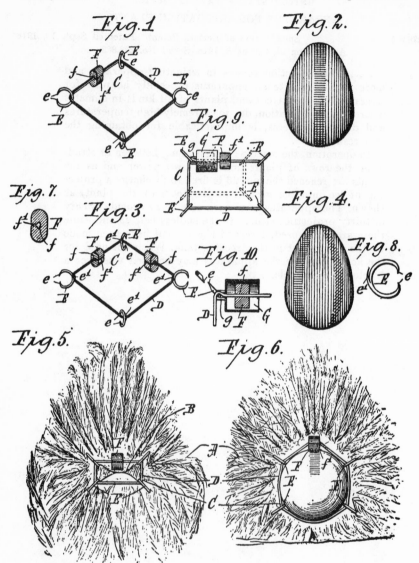

Fig.1

Fig.2.

Fig.9.

Fig.7.

Fig.3.

Fig.10.

Fig.4.

Fig.8.

Fig.5.

Fig.6.

Automatic Egg-Brander

UNITED STATES PATENT OFFICE

EGG-MARKING DEVICE

970,074   Specification of Letters Patent   Patented Sept. 13, 1910

Application filed April 18, 1910. Serial No. 556,049

. . . The primary object of my invention is the production of an egg marking-device bearing a marking-element or elements whereby the eggs laid by the hen to which the marking device is attached will be marked in a distinctive manner and whereby the laying capacities or qualities of each hen in a hennery can be easily ascertained.

Another object of my invention is the provision of a marking-device of this character which can be easily attached to the vent of a hen so that it will always be in place for marking an egg laid by said hen.

A further object of my invention is to so construct the marking-device that it will yield with the walls of the vent as the egg is being laid, thus permitting the egg to pass through the marking-device. . . .

When the egg is passed from the vent and through the supporting-band, said band is expanded, causing the marking element to be drawn out of the shield or protector, as best shown in Fig. 9, and as soon as the egg is laid, the walls of the vent return to normal position, as shown in Fig. 5, so that the supporting-band is relieved of tension and the marking-element enters the shield or protector. . . .

SALUTING DEVICE.

No. 556,248.							Patented Mar. 10, 1896.

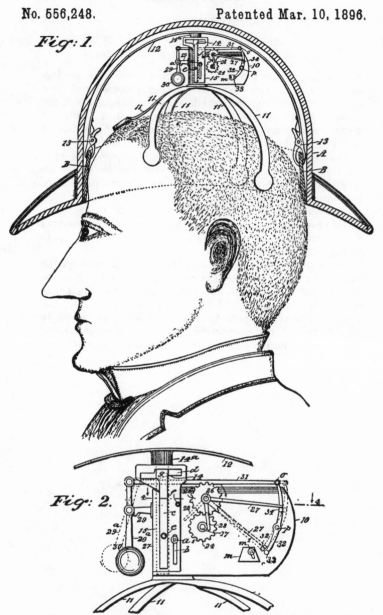

Fig: 1.

Fig: 2.

UNITED STATES PATENT OFFICE

SALUTING DEVICE

Specification forming part of Letters Patent No. 556,248, dated March 10, 1896
Application filed September 18, 1895. Serial No. 562,908. (No model)

. . . This invention relates to a novel device for automatically effecting polite salutations by the elevation and rotation of the hat on the head of the saluting party when said person bows to the person or persons saluted, the actuation of the hat being produced by mechanism therein and without the use of the hands in any manner. . . .

Should the wearer of the hat having the novel mechanism within it and engaging his head, as before explained, desire to salute another party, it will only be necessary for him to bow his head to cause the weight-block 30 to swing forwardly. The swinging of the block 30, as stated, will, by the consequent vibration rearwardly of the upper end of the arm 29^a, push the rod 31 backward and release the stud 34 on the rock-arm 32 from an engagement with the lifting-arm 27, so that the latter will, by stress of the spring 16, be forcibly rocked down into contact with the pin 33, as indicated by dotted lines in Fig. 2, the arm 28 having been correspondingly moved toward the lift-pin f, as also shown by dotted lines in the same figure. When the person making a salutation with the improvement applied to his hat resumes an erect posture after bowing, the weight 30 will swing back into a normal position, which will draw the upper end of the rock-arm 32 forwardly and move its lower end rearwardly far enough to release the arm 27 from the pin 33. The gear-wheel 25 will now be moved by the spring 16, so as to impinge the short arm 28 on the lower side of the stud f, which will cause the guide-plate 15 to slide upward, carrying the post 14 with it. Just before the arm 28 passes the stud f the detent-spring q will press its curved toe q' through the slot in the front plate of the case 10 and project said toe below the rounded lower end of the post 14. The lifting-arm 27 is now brought into contact with the pin e, and the pressure of the said arm on the pin e causes the post 14 to move upwardly in the depression c of the guide-plate 15 until it enters the slot d. The lift-pin e will now be swung through the rear portion of the cross-slot d by the arm 27, and by the impetus given to the pin and post 14 by said arm the post, bow-piece, and hat A will receive a rotary movement sufficient to bring the pin e into the depression c, when the gravity of the parts will cause the hat to drop into its normal position on the wearer's head. . . .

EMERGENCY RUBBER OVERSHOE

Filed June 8, 1923

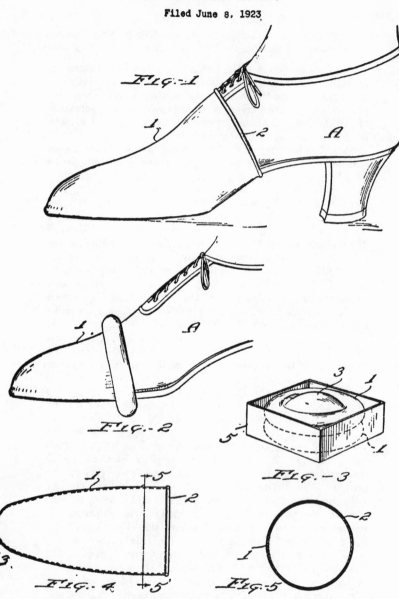

FIG.-1

FIG.-2

FIG.-3

FIG.-4

FIG.-5

UNITED STATES PATENT OFFICE

EMERGENCY RUBBER OVERSHOE

Patented Oct. 19, 1926   1,603,923

Application filed June 8, 1923. Serial No. 644,074

. . . This invention relates to a novel form of overshoe and has for its essential objects the provision of a very effective emergency rubber overshoe, adapted to be uniformly rolled up into a very small space and which may be so cheaply manufactured and sold as to invite the purchase and wearing of a pair on a single occasion, but which shall, at the same time, be sufficiently durable to be worn on numerous occasions if desired.

A further and important object is to so construct such an overshoe that when rolled into its compact space, it is ready for most immediate and easy application to the shoe and may be correspondingly easily removed by a rolling movement, bringing it again to the small compact form ready for subsequent wear.

A further object is to make the overshoe of very light construction using a very small amount of resilient material, thereby accomplishing economy and in addition causing the overshoe, by reason of its thinness and resiliency, to fit neatly in any position. To this end, I make the overshoe of substantially uniform thickness throughout, whereby it may be rolled on and will invariably position itself to neatly fit the shoe, and no regard need be given to the idea of rights or lefts, or even to the thought of which is top or bottom. Further advantageous and unique characteristics of my overshoe will appear in the following description, which relates to the accompanying drawings. The essential characteristics are summarized in the claims. . . .

When the overshoes are rolled up as indicated at Fig. 3, they take the form of a rolled ring with the portion 3 across the center thereof, and may be nested very neatly in a small package or box, such, for example, as indicated at 5. From this position they may be placed upon the shoes with great facility as follows:—

The ring is placed over the toe with the dome shaped portion 3 fitting over the convexity of the toe, and by a rolling motion between the thumb and finger, drawing rearwardly on the shoe, the rubber wall of the shoe is drawn tightly and evenly into position, until the bead 2 comes to the position shown in Fig 1, the operation requiring but a brief moment. . . .

ELECTRICAL BEDBUG EXTERMINATOR.

(Application filed Feb. 7, 1898.)

(No Model.)

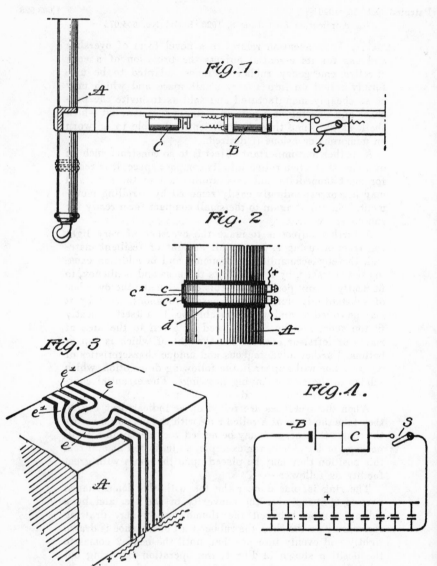

UNITED STATES PATENT OFFICE

ELECTRICAL BEDBUG-EXTERMINATOR

Specification forming part of Letters Patent No. 616,049, dated December 13, 1898
Application filed February 7, 1898. Serial No. 669,334. (No model)

. . . This invention relates to bedbug-exterminators; and it consists of electrical devices applied to bedsteads in such a manner that currents of electricity will be sent through the bodies of the bugs, which will either kill them or startle them, so that they will leave the bedstead. The electrical devices used consist of a battery, induction-coil, a switch, and a number of circuits leading to various locations on the bedstead, where are placed suitable circuit-terminals, arranged so that the bugs in moving about will close the circuit through their own bodies. . . .

The space c^2 between the rings is such that a bug in crossing from one to the other must close the circuit through its own body, and thus receive a current of electricity. If these rings are placed on a leg of the bedstead, an insect in climbing up will when it receives the shock more than likely change its mind and return in the direction whence it came. Another location where the contacts would be particularly efficient is at the joints between the side pieces and the head and foot boards. A perspective of such a joint is shown in Fig. 3. A pair of insulated contact-strips e and e' is placed along each of the contiguous edges of the joint and surrounding the joint on all sides. The polarities of these strips are so arranged that a positive and negative strip will be next to the respective edges, so that the insect in crossing a pair or the adjacent members of the two pairs will necessarily receive a current, which will either terminate its career at once or make it seek other locations. In like manner contact-strips in pairs, constituting the terminals of the circuit, may be located at various places on the bedstead or on the bedsprings, which will so harass the bugs as to cause them to shun the bed entirely. . . .

ALARM

Filed Dec. 6, 1927

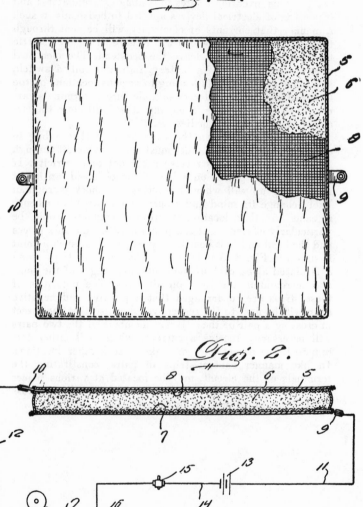

Bed-Wetting Alarm

UNITED STATES PATENT OFFICE

ALARM

Patented Aug. 5, 1930   1,772,282
Application filed December 6, 1927. Serial No. 238,028

. . . This invention relates to alarms, and has more particular reference to an electrical device of this kind adapted for use as an aid in curing persons of the habit of nocturnal urination or bed-wetting.

The primary object of the invention is to provide means for sounding an alarm when urination starts so as to awaken the sleeper before the bladder is emptied and thereby enable him or her to avoid material wetting of the bed. . . .

In operation, the filling material is normally dry and insulates the sheets 7 and 8 from each other so as to prevent sounding of the bell 17 even though the switch 15 is closed. When the sleeper begins to urinate, the urine runs through the casing 5 and conductor sheet 8 and saturates a portion of the filling material 6 entirely through to the sheet 7. The wetted portion of the material 6 is thus rendered conductive to electrically connect the sheets 7 and 8 and close the alarm circuit, whereby the bell 17 is caused to operate and awaken the sleeper before his or her bladder is emptied. By turning the switch 15 off, the alarm may be rendered silent, and by constructing the casing so that it may be opened, the wet filling material may be replaced by dry material to condition the device for re-use. . . .

COMBINED MATCH SAFE, PINCUSHION, AND TRAP.

No. 439,467.   Patented Oct. 28, 1890.

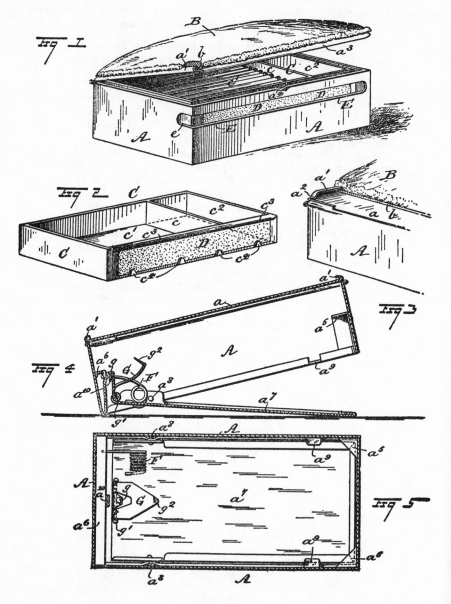

UNITED STATES PATENT OFFICE

COMBINED MATCH-SAFE, PINCUSHION, AND TRAP

Specification forming part of Letters Patent No. 439,467, dated October 28, 1890
Application filed May 27, 1890. Serial No. 353,345. (No model)

. . . My invention relates to a device adapted for a match-safe, pincushion, and trap, and has for its object to provide a simple, inexpensive, and compact structure capable of effective use for any of the purposes above specified.
. . .

When the device is to be set as a trap, the top pincushion B will be slid forward off the lid a of the main box or casing A and the match-tray C will be removed from the casing, and after the box-bottom is opened downward against the tension or torsional strain of the spring F and the lip g of the baited hook is set lightly upon the casing-catch a^{10} to hold the bottom open the casing, with its top a latched or closed, will be set on the floor or on a shelf, as shown in Fig. 4 of the drawings. When a mouse walks up the bottom a^7 and nibbles the bait on the hook G, the hook-lip g will be tripped from its detent a^{10}, and the spring F then will instantly close the bottom as the box or casing falls flat, and the mouse or animal will be caught in the trap. As the pincushion B is removed from the casing-top the casing, with the mouse in it, may be immersed in water to drown the animal without damaging the cushion, and after use of the device as a trap the match-tray C may again be put into the casing, and the cushion B will be again slipped into the guides a' on the casing top or lid, and the device is again ready for its most ordinary uses as a match-safe and pincushion, as will readily be understood.

METHOD OF PRESERVING THE DEAD.

APPLICATION FILED OCT. 13, 1903.

NO MODEL.

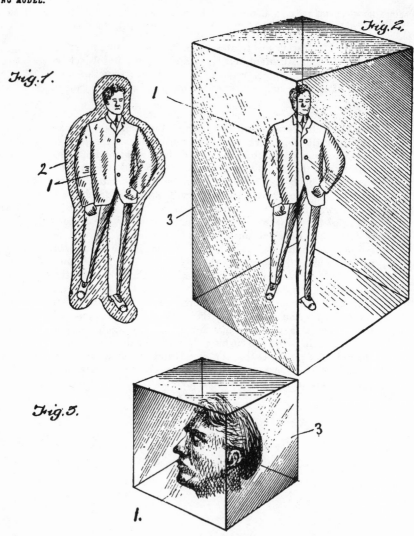

Fig. 1.

Fig. 2.

Fig. 3.

UNITED STATES PATENT OFFICE

METHOD OF PRESERVING THE DEAD

No. 748,284   Patented December 29, 1903

Specification forming part of Letters Patent No. 748,284, dated December 29, 1903
Application filed October 13, 1903. Serial No. 176,922. (No specimens)

. . . This invention relates to certain new and useful improvements in methods of preserving the dead; and it has for its object the provision of a means whereby a corpse may be hermetically incased within a block of transparent glass, whereby being effectually excluded from the air the corpse will be maintained for an indefinite period in a perfect and life-like condition, so that it will be prevented from decay and will at all times present a life-like appearance. . . .

In carrying out my process I first surround the corpse 1 with a thick layer 2 of sodium silicate or water-glass. After the corpse has been thus inclosed within the layer of water-glass it is allowed to remain for a short time within a compartment or chamber having a dry heated temperature, which will serve to evaporate the water from this incasing layer, after which molten glass is applied to the desired thickness. This outer layer of glass may be molded into a rectangular form 3, as shown in Fig. 2 of the drawings, or, if preferred, cylindrical or other forms may be substituted for the rectangular block which I have illustrated. In Fig. 3 I have shown the head only of the corpse as incased within the transparent block of glass, it being at once evident that the head alone may be preserved in this manner, if preferred. . . .

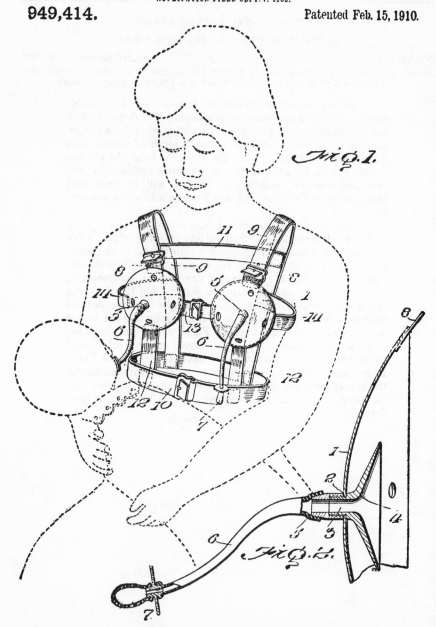

Fig. 1.

Fig. 2.

UNITED STATES PATENT OFFICE

NURSING ATTACHMENT

949,414   Specification of Letters Patent   Patented Feb. 15, 1910
Application filed September 7, 1909. Serial No. 516,336

. . . The primary object of this invention is an improved construction of device for use by mothers with nursing infants, and designed particularly to avoid unpleasant and embarrassing situations in which mothers are sometimes placed in public places by the necessary exposure of the breast in suckling the child.

With this and other objects in view, as will more fully appear as the description proceeds, the invention consists essentially in a nursing attachment designed to be worn over the breasts and arranged for the detachable connection thereto of the nipple on a tube of any desired length, the nipple or nipples, according to whether there be one or two employed, being worn inside of the shirtwaist or other outer garment and it being only necessary when the child is to be nursed, to slip the nipple out of the waist, thereby avoiding the necessity of exposing the person. . . .

In the practical use of the device, the shields 1 are adjusted over the breasts with the cups 4 directly over the nipples and the cap or caps 5 are then attached, the nursing nipples 7 and all other parts being hidden beneath the wearer's waist. Whenever the child requires nursing it is only necessary to slide one of the nursing nipples 7 out from the waist and the child can obtain its proper nourishment without the exposure of the mother's person and the consequent embarrassment which is thus often occasioned. . . .

1,051,684.

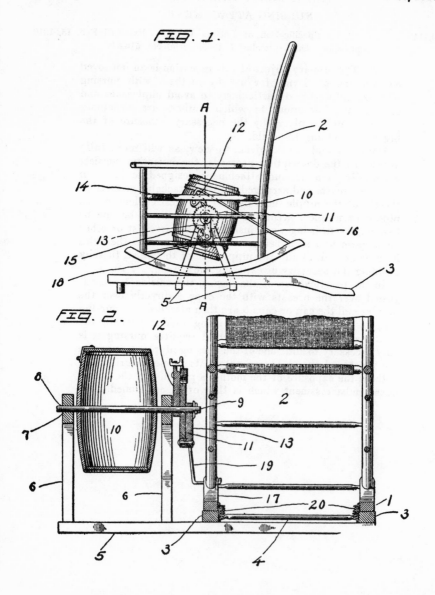

FIG. 1.

FIG. 2.

UNITED STATES PATENT OFFICE

CHURN

1,051,684   Specification of Letters Patent   Patented Jan. 28, 1913

Application filed June 28, 1912. Serial No. 706,431

. . . This invention relates to improvements in churns and especially with reference to improvements in means, actuated by a rocking chair to operate a churn, so that a churn may be operated by a person seated and rocking in a rocking chair, the invention consisting in the construction, combination and arrangement of devices, hereinafter described and claimed. . . .

When the chair is rocked, the rods 18—19 cause the arms 12—13 to be oscillated and to move simultaneously in the same direction, so that while the pawl 14 moves rearwardly on the upper side of the ratchet wheel and turns the latter the pawl 15 will slip on the under side of the ratchet wheel, and in the reverse movement of the said arms 12—13, the pawl 15 by engagement with the lower side of the ratchet wheel will turn the latter while the pawl 14 slips on the upper side thereof. Hence, the ratchet wheel is rotated in one direction and causes the churn body to correspondingly rotate. . . .

1,016,164.

Patented Jan. 30, 1912.

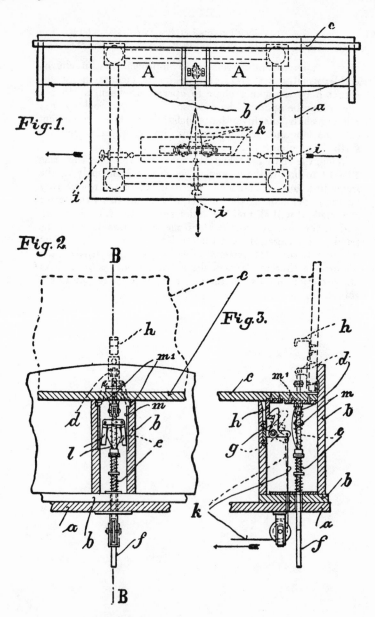

Fig.1.

Fig.2.

Fig.3.

UNITED STATES PATENT OFFICE

DEVICE FOR PROTECTING THE MEMBERS OF A COURT ASSEMBLY

1,016,164   Specification of Letters Patent   Patented Jan. 30, 1912
Application filed March 11, 1910. Serial No. 548,755

. . . The present invention relates to a device for the protection of the members of a court assembly against attempts upon their lives, such attempts being of frequent occurrence at the giving of verdicts.

The invention consists in the provision of a bullet-proof plate which is hingedly connected to the head piece of the court table and which, while being normally maintained in horizontal position, is actuated by a spring so as to be raised into vertical, protecting position as soon as released, such releasing being effected by the actuating knobs arranged in various places around the table. . . .

To the back side of the head piece b of a court table a, a bullet-proof plate c is hingedly connected. A bracket d on the underside of said plate is pivotally connected to a rod f which is slidably guided in the head piece b and encircled by a helical spring e, the latter abutting against a collar on the rod and tending to raise the rod for bringing the plate c into vertical position, as shown dotted in Fig. 3. The plate c is normally maintained in horizontal position by means of a pivoted catch g engaging a bent finger h on the underside of the plate. The catch g is of bell-crank-shape and can be actuated by means of a cord k so as to release the plate. This cord is guided by means of sheaves under the table top and branched off to the various seats of the table where the branches are connected to actuating knobs i. It is thus possible for any of the persons seated around the table to release the protecting plate which, as soon as released, assumes a vertical, protecting position. The rod f is also provided with pivoted spring-actuated detents l the ends of which slide in grooves m in vertical members of the head piece b and snap into recesses m^1 so as to secure the plate c in raised position. . . .

SANITARY COW STALL

Filed March 22 , 1924

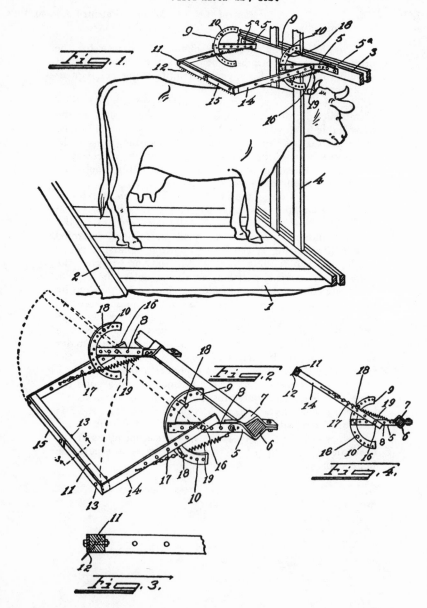

Device for Inhibiting Certain Acts in Cows

UNITED STATES PATENT OFFICE

SANITARY COW STALL

Patented Oct. 21, 1924   1,512,610

Application filed March 22, 1924. Serial No. 701,040

. . . My invention relates to cow stalls in which provision is made for preserving them in a clean condition.

It is a known fact that where a pointed object is arranged closely above the back of a cow, the animal will not be able to hump up while in the stall until she backs up far enough at the time of humping. As a result stalls may be kept clean from droppings.

The above known fact has been utilized in several instances as a basis for devices to be used in dairy barns where cleanliness of the animal, and particularly her udders, is a matter of vital importance. The object of my invention is to improve upon, and render more practical devices for such purpose. . . .

In use the operator will set the pivot bolts and the stop pins at such a point that the frame will lie closely above the proper point on the cow's back to result in pronging the cow with the pins of the pin bar, should she hump up, without backing to a position where the stall will not be soiled. . . .

When taking the cow out of the stall the dairyman merely throws up the frame, past center, whereupon it will spring up well beyond any chance contact with the animal, and when the cow is back in her place, he will drop the frame, so as to bring the pins into position, ready to interfere with the cow soiling her stall, by inhibiting the act of humping up. . . .

FEEDING DEVICE FOR POULTRY.
APPLICATION FILED MAR. 21, 1906.

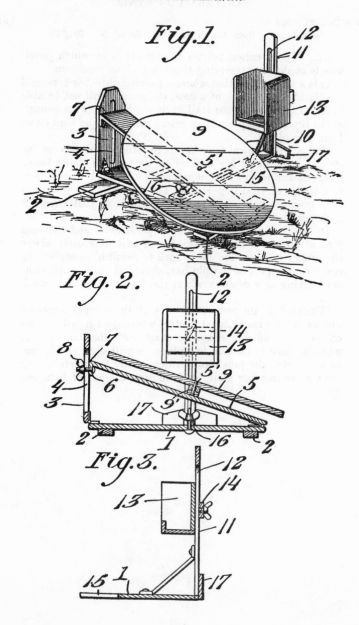

Fig.1.

Fig.2.

Fig.3.

UNITED STATES PATENT OFFICE

FEEDING DEVICE FOR POULTRY

No. 828,227   Specification of Letters Patent   Patented Aug. 7, 1906
Application filed March 21, 1906. Serial No. 307,270

. . . The invention relates to an improvement in feeding devices for poultry, comprehending specifically an exerciser and feeder in the use of which the fowls secure a beneficial amount of exercise in feeding.

The main object of the present invention is the production of a device so constructed and arranged that the fowl in order to secure the food carried by the stretcher is compelled to undergo increased exercise as compared with the ordinary manner of feeding, whereby the fowls in the act of feeding are given that degree of exercise best suited to insure their proper condition. . . .

In operation the fowls desiring the food in the box and stepping upon the platform cause the same to revolve under their weight, with the result that they are compelled to move rapidly forward to maintain such position on the platform as will enable them to reach the food in the box. It is of course to be understood that in all relative positions of the parts the supporting-plate 5, and therefore the platform, is disposed at an angle to the base 1, whereby to provide for the necessary movement of the platform under the weight of the fowl. The angular adjustment of the plate 5, however, will permit of the angular arrangment of the supporting-plate being adjusted to accommodate the device to the weight of the particular species of fowls, it being of course evident that the heavier the fowl the less the relative inclination of the platform, as it is only desired that the weight of the fowl cause a revolution of the platform during the attempting of the fowl to reach the feed-box. . . .

FIG.1.

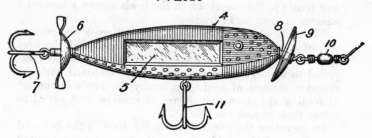

FIG.2.

UNITED STATES PATENT OFFICE

ARTIFICIAL FISH-BAIT

1,180,758   Specification of Letters Patent   Patented Apr. 25, 1916
Application filed April 23, 1915. Serial No. 23,351

. . . My invention relates more particularly to artificial baits for trawling, and its primary objects are to make the bait more attractive to the fish, to secure its proper position in the water, to provide a convenient and effective hanging of the hooks, and to generally improve the structure and operation of trawling baits. . . .

The attractiveness of the bait for the fish is increased by making the disks 6 and 9 of highly polished metal. The glitter and flashing lights occasioned by these and by the mirror are well known attractives; but the mirror 5 is an additional feature that insures the effectiveness of the bait in the following manner: A male fish seeing his image upon looking therein will appear to see another fish approach it from the opposite side with the intent to seize the bait, and this will not only arouse his warlike spirit, but also appeal to his greed, and he will seize the bait quickly in order to defeat the approaching rival. In case the fish is suspected of cowardice I may make the mirror of convex form, as shown at 5^a, in order that the rival or antagonist may appear to be smaller. In the case of a female fish the attractiveness of a mirror is too well known to need discussion. Thus the bait appeals to the ruling passion of both sexes, and renders it very certain and efficient in operation. . . .

FISHING APPARATUS.

Patented Feb. 20, 1894.

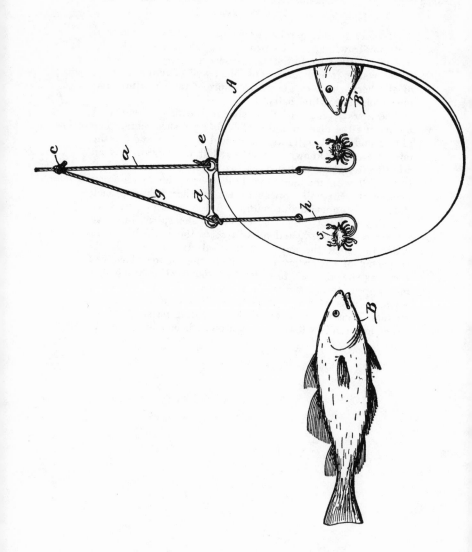

Double Bait

UNITED STATES PATENT OFFICE

FISHING APPARATUS

Specification forming part of Letters Patent No. 515,001, dated February 20, 1894
Application filed April 29, 1893. Serial No. 472,314. (No model)

. . . This invention relates to that class of devices used as decoys in fishing, the object of it being to induce the fish to take the bait more readily. It is illustrated in the accompanying drawing, which may be explained as follows:

. . . In using the apparatus, a bait s, (represented in this case as a small crab) is put on the hook h, and let down into the water with the mirror which serves as a sinker, until its lower edge just touches the bottom. In this position, the least pull on the hook on the branch line, will be felt very plainly by the hand at the upper end of the taut main line a. In this position, as shown in the drawing, the fish B, when approaching the bait s, will see the reflection B′, of himself in the mirror, also coming for the reflection of the bait s', and will be made bolder by the supposed companionship, and more eager to take the bait before his competitor seizes it. He will lose his caution, and take the bait with a recklessness that greatly increases the chances of his being caught on the hook. The reflection of light from the mirror in the water, will have in some degree the effect that the lighted torch has in some well known kinds of fishing, of attracting fish to the bait, and the light reflected by the mirror upon the bait, will make it more conspicuous. . . .

Fire-Escape.

No. 221,855.　　　　Patented Nov. 18, 1879.

UNITED STATES PATENT OFFICE

IMPROVEMENT IN FIRE-ESCAPES

Specification forming part of Letters Patent No. 221,855, dated November 18, 1879
Application filed March 26, 1879

. . . This invention relates to an improved fire-escape or safety device, by which a person may safely jump out of the window of a burning building from any height, and land, without injury and without the least damage, on the ground; and it consists of a parachute attached, in suitable manner, to the upper part of the body, in combination with overshoes having elastic bottom pads of suitable thickness to take up the concussion with the ground. . . .

Fig. 1.

Fig. 2.

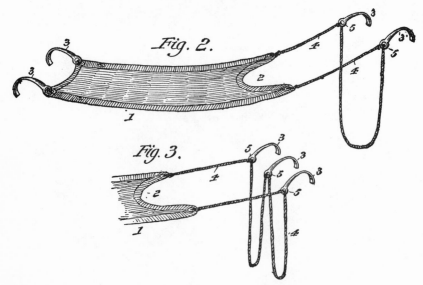

Fig. 3.

UNITED STATES PATENT OFFICE

HAMMOCK

Specification forming part of Letters Patent No. 400,131, dated March 26, 1889
Application filed June 19, 1888. Serial No. 277,573. (No model)

. . . This invention relates to an improvement in hammocks, and has special reference to a hammock so constructed that it can be slung from and used with the backs of the seats of ordinary railway passenger-cars.

The invention has for its object to provide a means whereby passengers who are obliged to travel in ordinary passenger-cars at night may be able to sleep with ease and comfort. . . .

Instead of employing the hammock as shown in Fig. 1, the occupant may recline practically at full length, by attaching the hooks on the rope 4 to the upper edge of the back of the adjacent seat after the back has been turned over. In this case the rope 4 will have been drawn through the eyes 3, thereby drawing up the loop, and the feet and lower portion of the legs of the occupant of the hammock will rest on the car-seat. . . .

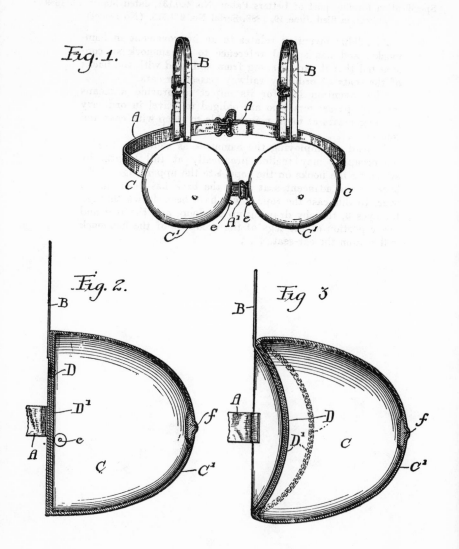

UNITED STATES PATENT OFFICE

BUST-FORM

1,033,788   Specification of Letters Patent   Patented July 30, 1912

Application filed August 6, 1908. Serial No. 447,194

. . . The invention relates to bust forms and designs to provide an improved device, designed to supply any natural deficiency of form and to support the breasts, which will effectively give the appearance of the natural bust, and which may be readily fitted to different breasts and worn with comfort. . . .

The invention further designs to construct the bust-forms so that when worn, they will not have the appearance of lifeless members, but will vibrate responsively to movements of the wearer. . . .

In use, when pneumatic pads are inflated and covered by garments, the bosom is sometimes rather lifeless in appearance, due to the inflated pads which do not readily or freely respond to the movements of the wearer's bosom. To overcome this appearance, a weight f is molded into the front of the casing C, and under the influence of the body is suspended at the front of the pad and sets the front in motion so that it will vibrate freely in response to any movement of the body of the wearer. . . .

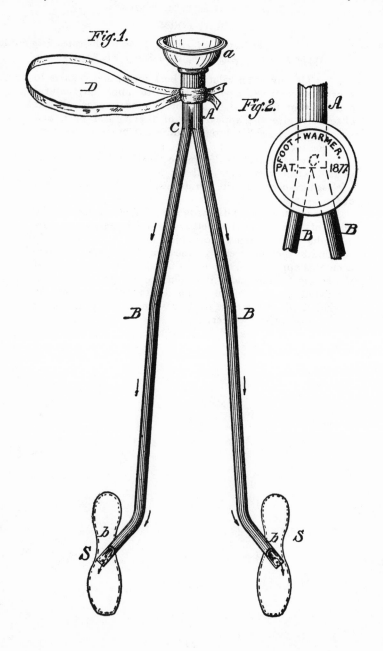

Fig.1.

Fig.2.

Pedal Calorificator

UNITED STATES PATENT OFFICE

IMPROVEMENT IN FOOT-WARMERS

Specification forming part of Letters Patent No. 186,962, dated February 6, 1877
Application filed January 16, 1877

. . . Be it known that I have made a new and useful invention in a "Pedal Calorificator" or "Foot-Warmer." . . .

It is a well-established fact that our lungs constitute the laboratory of nature, within which—by a condensing process—animal heat is generated, and afterward conveyed and distributed to other portions of our bodies by the action of the heart and circulation of the blood; that, for mechanical reasons the supply to the extremities—the hands and feet—on account of their distance from the center of heat, is more or less deficient, and, consequently, they suffer most when exposed to severe outward cold; the feet, especially, by reason of their immediate contact, in winter weather, with cold floors, as in railroad-cars and other vehicles, and with the frozen ground and icy sidewalks.

Now, I find, by personal experiment, that by breathing for a short time on the bulb of a thermometer I am enabled to raise the mercury to 88° Fahrenheit—only 10° below blood-heat—which I, therefore, assume to be the natural temperature of the breath, and . . . which, in the action of breathing, is totally dissipated and lost in the open air.

My invention aims at economizing and utilizing this wasted heat by any simple contrivance for conveying it to our feet, where it is so much needed. . . .

I have found, by actual experience, that the tubes in a short time become warmed by the body, so that little heat of the breath is lost in its passage to the feet; that, accordingly, the air I find is delivered in boot or shoe with a temperature of about 84° Fahrenheit—a loss of only 4°.

After a few sharp blasts of breath at the beginning—which may be repeated at intervals—it becomes only necessary to inhale naturally with closed, and exhale with open, lips—an easy process, which I have ascertained practically may be kept up a long time, as, for example, for miles on a railroad-car, without much personal inconvenience. . . .

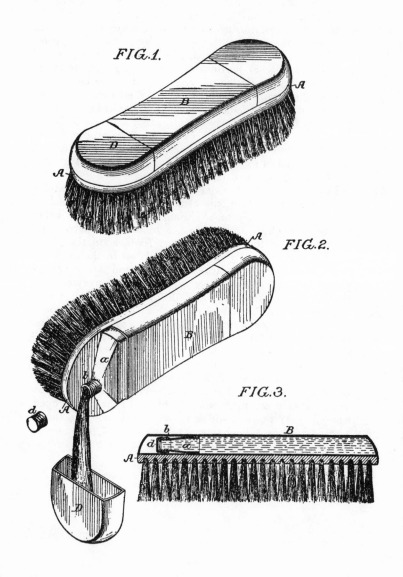

FIG.1.

FIG.2.

FIG.3.

Morning Pick-Me-Up Device

UNITED STATES PATENT OFFICE

COMBINED CLOTHES-BRUSH, FLASK, AND DRINKING-CUP

Specification forming part of Letters Patent No. 490,964, dated January 31, 1893
Application filed November 4, 1892. Serial No. 450,926. (No model)

. . . The object of my invention is to so construct a combined clothes brush, liquor flask, and drinking cup, as to provide for the compact disposal of the parts and thus attain the desired object without unduly increasing the size of the brush. . . .

Fitting snugly to the base of the contracted neck *a* of the flask is a cup D which, when applied to the neck of the flask as shown in Fig. 1, presents an outer surface flush with that of the flask and fitting snugly against the brush block, this cup conforming to the shape of that part of the block A which it covers, so that when the cup is in place on the flask the brush presents substantially the same appearance as an ordinary clothes brush, the cup, however, being readily removed when it is desired to use the same for drinking purposes, as shown in Fig. 2. . . .

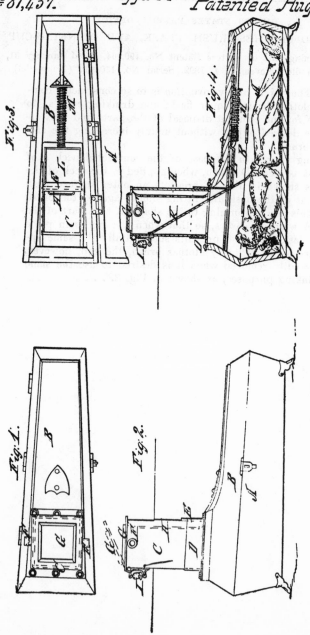

Fig. 3.

Fig. 4.

Fig. 1.

Fig. 2.

UNITED STATES PATENT OFFICE

IMPROVED BURIAL-CASE

Specification forming part of Letters Patent No. 81,437, dated August 25, 1868

. . . The nature of this invention consists in placing on the lid of the coffin, and directly over the face of the body laid therein, a square tube, which extends from the coffin up through and over the surface of the grave, said tube containing a ladder and a cord, one end of said cord being placed in the hand of the person laid in the coffin, and the other end of said cord being attached to a bell on the top of the square tube, so that, should a person be interred ere life is extinct, he can, on recovery to consciousness, ascend from the grave and the coffin by the ladder; or, if not able to ascend by said ladder, ring the bell, thereby giving an alarm, and thus save himself from premature burial and death; and if, on inspection, life is extinct, the tube is withdrawn, the sliding door closed, and the tube used for a similar purpose. . . .

1,303,851.

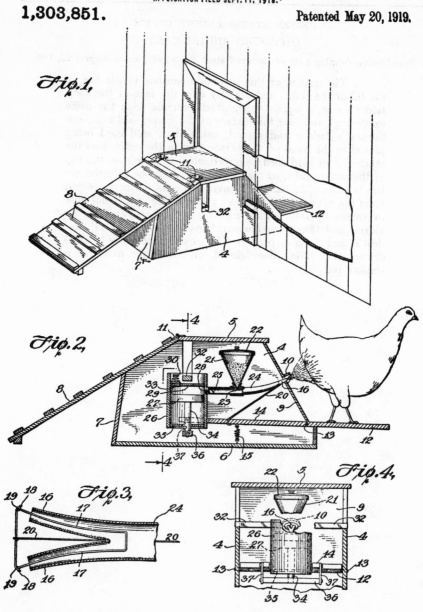

UNITED STATES PATENT OFFICE

POULTRY-DISINFECTOR

1,303,851   Specification of Letters Patent   Patented May 20, 1919
Application filed September 11, 1918. Serial No. 253,621

... This invention is a novel poultry disinfector, that is to say, an apparatus adapted to dust an insecticide powder, or to spray any other disinfectant upon live poultry. The principal object of the present invention is to afford such an apparatus which will be wholly self-acting and requiring very little attention from the poultry keeper, and which as well will be simple in structure, durable, effective in action and convenient of use. ...

The illustrated embodiment of the present invention discloses a compact and portable apparatus which can be placed where desired, for example, in the entrance to the hen-house or a runway, and as will be seen it is adapted to operate in both directions, that is, on poultry coming and going so that they are sprayed at both front and rear. The apparatus preferably contains a box-like structure from the front of which projects a balanced low platform across or upon which a hen may walk or hop in entering or leaving the hen-house. Within the casing are the pneumatic sprayer directed outwardly at the front, and the mechanism for operating and controlling the same. ...

By this arrangement, when the hen jumps on the front part 12 of the platform, the rear or interior end causes the piston to rise thus forcing air from the cylinder through the pipe 24, so as to carry the powder from the hopper 21 to the nozzle 16, whence it is sprayed upon the fowl. When the air is under pressure part of it will pass through the pinhole 23 into the hopper thus stirring up the disinfectant, and such air forced into the hopper promptly returns thus insuring passage of a suitable amount of powder into the pipe 24 at each operation. ...

Life Preserver.

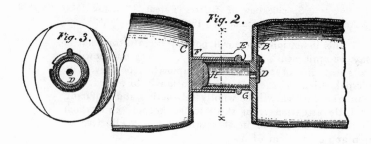

Fig. 3.   Fig. 2.

Fig. 1.

UNITED STATES PATENT OFFICE

IMPROVEMENT IN LIFE-PRESERVERS

Letters Patent No. 100,906, dated March 15, 1870
The Schedule referred to in these Letters Patent and making part of the same.

. . . My invention relates to life-preservers, and consists of a circular hollow cylinder, made out of any light, flexible, air-tight material, of sufficient length to extend around the neck, and having attached to one of its ends a short tube with a hinged valve at its bottom, and to the other a similar tube of the proper size to slide within the former, and in providing these tubes with a bayonet-clasp. . . .

In using a life-preserver thus constructed, it is only necessary to remove the stopper H and fill the cylinder, by forcing air or gas through the tube G and past the valve D, and when filled to insert the stopper H, and fasten the cylinder about the neck.

The valve D should be so constructed and arranged that, with the aid of the pressure of air or gas against it within the cylinder, together with the stopper H at the end of the tube G, there can be no escape of the air or gas from the interior of the cylinder.

It is obvious that a device thus constructed, arranged, and applied, will keep the head of the wearer above the water, and thus saved from drowning. . . .

FISH LURE

Filed Nov. 19, 1927

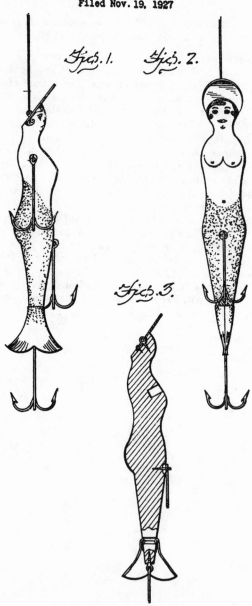

Fig. 1.   Fig. 2.

Fig. 3.

UNITED STATES PATENT OFFICE

DESIGN FOR A FISH LURE

Patented Mar. 20, 1928   Des. 74,759

Application filed November 19, 1927. Serial No. 24,209. Term of patent 7 years

... Be it known that I ... have invented a new, original, and ornamental Design for a Fish Lure, of which the following is a specification, reference being had to the accompanying drawing, forming part thereof.

Figure 1 is a side elevation of a fish lure, showing my new design.

Figure 2 is a front elevation thereof, and

Figure 3 is a longitudinal sectional view thereof. . . .

VISUAL ILLUSIONS: THEIR CAUSES, CHARACTERISTICS, AND APPLICATIONS, Matthew Luckiesh. Thorough description and discussion of optical illusion, geometric and perspective, particularly; size and shape distortions, illusions of color, of motion; natural illusions; use of illusion in art and magic, industry, etc. Most useful today with op art, also for classical art. Scores of effects illustrated. Introduction by William H. Ittleson. 100 illustrations. xxi + 252pp.
21530-X Paperbound $2.00

A HANDBOOK OF ANATOMY FOR ART STUDENTS, Arthur Thomson. Thorough, virtually exhaustive coverage of skeletal structure, musculature, etc. Full text, supplemented by anatomical diagrams and drawings and by photographs of undraped figures. Unique in its comparison of male and female forms, pointing out differences of contour, texture, form. 211 figures, 40 drawings, 86 photographs. xx + 459pp. 5⅜ x 8⅜.
21163-0 Paperbound $3.50

150 MASTERPIECES OF DRAWING, Selected by Anthony Toney. Full page reproductions of drawings from the early 16th to the end of the 18th century, all beautifully reproduced: Rembrandt, Michelangelo, Dürer, Fragonard, Urs, Graf, Wouwerman, many others. First-rate browsing book, model book for artists. xviii + 150pp. 8⅜ x 11¼.
21032-4 Paperbound $2.50

THE LATER WORK OF AUBREY BEARDSLEY, Aubrey Beardsley. Exotic, erotic, ironic masterpieces in full maturity: Comedy Ballet, Venus and Tannhauser, Pierrot, Lysistrata, Rape of the Lock, Savoy material, Ali Baba, Volpone, etc. This material revolutionized the art world, and is still powerful, fresh, brilliant. With *The Early Work,* all Beardsley's finest work. 174 plates, 2 in color. xiv + 176pp. 8⅛ x 11.
21817-1 Paperbound $3.00

DRAWINGS OF REMBRANDT, Rembrandt van Rijn. Complete reproduction of fabulously rare edition by Lippmann and Hofstede de Groot, completely reedited, updated, improved by Prof. Seymour Slive, Fogg Museum. Portraits, Biblical sketches, landscapes, Oriental types, nudes, episodes from classical mythology—All Rembrandt's fertile genius. Also selection of drawings by his pupils and followers. "Stunning volumes," *Saturday Review.* 550 illustrations. lxxviii + 552pp. 9⅛ x 12¼.
21485-0, 21486-9 Two volumes, Paperbound $10.00

THE DISASTERS OF WAR, Francisco Goya. One of the masterpieces of Western civilization—83 etchings that record Goya's shattering, bitter reaction to the Napoleonic war that swept through Spain after the insurrection of 1808 and to war in general. Reprint of the first edition, with three additional plates from Boston's Museum of Fine Arts. All plates facsimile size. Introduction by Philip Hofer, Fogg Museum. v + 97pp. 9⅜ x 8¼.
21872-4 Paperbound $2.00

GRAPHIC WORKS OF ODILON REDON. Largest collection of Redon's graphic works ever assembled: 172 lithographs, 28 etchings and engravings, 9 drawings. These include some of his most famous works. All the plates from *Odilon Redon: oeuvre graphique complet,* plus additional plates. New introduction and caption translations by Alfred Werner. 209 illustrations. xxvii + 209pp. 9⅛ x 12¼.
21966-8 Paperbound $4.00

DESIGN BY ACCIDENT; A BOOK OF "ACCIDENTAL EFFECTS" FOR ARTISTS AND DESIGNERS, James F. O'Brien. Create your own unique, striking, imaginative effects by "controlled accident" interaction of materials: paints and lacquers, oil and water based paints, splatter, crackling materials, shatter, similar items. Everything you do will be different; first book on this limitless art, so useful to both fine artist and commercial artist. Full instructions. 192 plates showing "accidents," 8 in color. viii + 215pp. 8⅜ x 11¼.   21942-9 Paperbound $3.50

THE BOOK OF SIGNS, Rudolf Koch. Famed German type designer draws 493 beautiful symbols: religious, mystical, alchemical, imperial, property marks, runes, etc. Remarkable fusion of traditional and modern. Good for suggestions of timelessness, smartness, modernity. Text. vi + 104pp. 6⅛ x 9¼.
20162-7 Paperbound $1.25

HISTORY OF INDIAN AND INDONESIAN ART, Ananda K. Coomaraswamy. An unabridged republication of one of the finest books by a great scholar in Eastern art. Rich in descriptive material, history, social backgrounds; Sunga reliefs, Rajput paintings, Gupta temples, Burmese frescoes, textiles, jewelry, sculpture, etc. 400 photos. viii + 423pp. 6⅜ x 9¾.   21436-2 Paperbound $5.00

PRIMITIVE ART, Franz Boas. America's foremost anthropologist surveys textiles, ceramics, woodcarving, basketry, metalwork, etc.; patterns, technology, creation of symbols, style origins. All areas of world, but very full on Northwest Coast Indians. More than 350 illustrations of baskets, boxes, totem poles, weapons, etc. 378 pp.
20025-6 Paperbound $3.00

THE GENTLEMAN AND CABINET MAKER'S DIRECTOR, Thomas Chippendale. Full reprint (third edition, 1762) of most influential furniture book of all time, by master cabinetmaker. 200 plates, illustrating chairs, sofas, mirrors, tables, cabinets, plus 24 photographs of surviving pieces. Biographical introduction by N. Bienenstock. vi + 249pp. 9⅞ x 12¾.   21601-2 Paperbound $4.00

AMERICAN ANTIQUE FURNITURE, Edgar G. Miller, Jr. The basic coverage of all American furniture before 1840. Individual chapters cover type of furniture—clocks, tables, sideboards, etc.—chronologically, with inexhaustible wealth of data. More than 2100 photographs, all identified, commented on. Essential to all early American collectors. Introduction by H. E. Keyes. vi + 1106pp. 7⅞ x 10¾.
21599-7, 21600-4 Two volumes, Paperbound $11.00

PENNSYLVANIA DUTCH AMERICAN FOLK ART, Henry J. Kauffman. 279 photos, 28 drawings of tulipware, Fraktur script, painted tinware, toys, flowered furniture, quilts, samplers, hex signs, house interiors, etc. Full descriptive text. Excellent for tourist, rewarding for designer, collector. Map. 146pp. 7⅞ x 10¾.
21205-X Paperbound $2.50

EARLY NEW ENGLAND GRAVESTONE RUBBINGS, Edmund V. Gillon, Jr. 43 photographs, 226 carefully reproduced rubbings show heavily symbolic, sometimes macabre early gravestones, up to early 19th century. Remarkable early American primitive art, occasionally strikingly beautiful; always powerful. Text. xxvi + 207pp. 8⅜ x 11¼.   21380-3 Paperbound $3.50

ALPHABETS AND ORNAMENTS, Ernst Lehner. Well-known pictorial source for decorative alphabets, script examples, cartouches, frames, decorative title pages, calligraphic initials, borders, similar material. 14th to 19th century, mostly European. Useful in almost any graphic arts designing, varied styles. 750 illustrations. 256pp. 7 x 10. 21905-4 Paperbound $4.00

PAINTING: A CREATIVE APPROACH, Norman Colquhoun. For the beginner simple guide provides an instructive approach to painting: major stumbling blocks for beginner; overcoming them, technical points; paints and pigments; oil painting; watercolor and other media and color. New section on "plastic" paints. Glossary. Formerly *Paint Your Own Pictures.* 221pp. 22000-1 Paperbound $1.75

THE ENJOYMENT AND USE OF COLOR, Walter Sargent. Explanation of the relations between colors themselves and between colors in nature and art, including hundreds of little-known facts about color values, intensities, effects of high and low illumination, complementary colors. Many practical hints for painters, references to great masters. 7 color plates, 29 illustrations. x + 274pp.
20944-X Paperbound $2.75

THE NOTEBOOKS OF LEONARDO DA VINCI, compiled and edited by Jean Paul Richter. 1566 extracts from original manuscripts reveal the full range of Leonardo's versatile genius: all his writings on painting, sculpture, architecture, anatomy, astronomy, geography, topography, physiology, mining, music, etc., in both Italian and English, with 186 plates of manuscript pages and more than 500 additional drawings. Includes studies for the Last Supper, the lost Sforza monument, and other works. Total of xlvii + 866pp. $7\frac{7}{8}$ x $10\frac{3}{4}$.
22572-0, 22573-9 Two volumes, Paperbound $10.00

MONTGOMERY WARD CATALOGUE OF 1895. Tea gowns, yards of flannel and pillow-case lace, stereoscopes, books of gospel hymns, the New Improved Singer Sewing Machine, side saddles, milk skimmers, straight-edged razors, high-button shoes, spittoons, and on and on . . . listing some 25,000 items, practically all illustrated. Essential to the shoppers of the 1890's, it is our truest record of the spirit of the period. Unaltered reprint of Issue No. 57, Spring and Summer 1895. Introduction by Boris Emmet. Innumerable illustrations. xiii + 624pp. $8\frac{1}{2}$ x $11\frac{5}{8}$.
22377-9 Paperbound $6.95

THE CRYSTAL PALACE EXHIBITION ILLUSTRATED CATALOGUE (LONDON, 1851). One of the wonders of the modern world—the Crystal Palace Exhibition in which all the nations of the civilized world exhibited their achievements in the arts and sciences—presented in an equally important illustrated catalogue. More than 1700 items pictured with accompanying text—ceramics, textiles, cast-iron work, carpets, pianos, sleds, razors, wall-papers, billiard tables, beehives, silverware and hundreds of other artifacts—represent the focal point of Victorian culture in the Western World. Probably the largest collection of Victorian decorative art ever assembled—indispensable for antiquarians and designers. Unabridged republication of the Art-Journal Catalogue of the Great Exhibition of 1851, with all terminal essays. New introduction by John Gloag, F.S.A. xxxiv + 426pp. 9 x 12.
22503-8 Paperbound $4.50

A HISTORY OF COSTUME, Carl Köhler. Definitive history, based on surviving pieces of clothing primarily, and paintings, statues, etc. secondarily. Highly readable text, supplemented by 594 illustrations of costumes of the ancient Mediterranean peoples, Greece and Rome, the Teutonic prehistoric period; costumes of the Middle Ages, Renaissance, Baroque, 18th and 19th centuries. Clear, measured patterns are provided for many clothing articles. Approach is practical throughout. Enlarged by Emma von Sichart. 464pp. 21030-8 Paperbound $3.50

ORIENTAL RUGS, ANTIQUE AND MODERN, Walter A. Hawley. A complete and authoritative treatise on the Oriental rug—where they are made, by whom and how, designs and symbols, characteristics in detail of the six major groups, how to distinguish them and how to buy them. Detailed technical data is provided on periods, weaves, warps, wefts, textures, sides, ends and knots, although no technical background is required for an understanding. 11 color plates, 80 halftones, 4 maps. vi + 320pp. 6⅛ x 9⅛. 22366-3 Paperbound $5.00

TEN BOOKS ON ARCHITECTURE, Vitruvius. By any standards the most important book on architecture ever written. Early Roman discussion of aesthetics of building, construction methods, orders, sites, and every other aspect of architecture has inspired, instructed architecture for about 2,000 years. Stands behind Palladio, Michelangelo, Bramante, Wren, countless others. Definitive Morris H. Morgan translation. 68 illustrations. xii + 331pp. 20645-9 Paperbound $3.00

THE FOUR BOOKS OF ARCHITECTURE, Andrea Palladio. Translated into every major Western European language in the two centuries following its publication in 1570, this has been one of the most influential books in the history of architecture. Complete reprint of the 1738 Isaac Ware edition. New introduction by Adolf Placzek, Columbia Univ. 216 plates. xxii + 110pp. of text. 9½ x 12¾. 21308-0 Clothbound $10.00

STICKS AND STONES: A STUDY OF AMERICAN ARCHITECTURE AND CIVILIZATION, Lewis Mumford.One of the great classics of American cultural history. American architecture from the medieval-inspired earliest forms to the early 20th century; evolution of structure and style, and reciprocal influences on environment. 21 photographic illustrations. 238pp. 20202-X Paperbound $2.00

THE AMERICAN BUILDER'S COMPANION, Asher Benjamin. The most widely used early 19th century architectural style and source book, for colonial up into Greek Revival periods. Extensive development of geometry of carpentering, construction of sashes, frames, doors, stairs; plans and elevations of domestic and other buildings. Hundreds of thousands of houses were built according to this book, now invaluable to historians, architects, restorers, etc. 1827 edition. 59 plates. 114pp. 7⅞ x 10¾. 22236-5 Paperbound $3.50

DUTCH HOUSES IN THE HUDSON VALLEY BEFORE 1776, Helen Wilkinson Reynolds. The standard survey of the Dutch colonial house and outbuildings, with constructional features, decoration, and local history associated with individual homesteads. Introduction by Franklin D. Roosevelt. Map. 150 illustrations. 469pp. 6⅝ x 9¼. 21469-9 Paperbound $4.00

THE ARCHITECTURE OF COUNTRY HOUSES, Andrew J. Downing. Together with Vaux's *Villas and Cottages* this is the basic book for Hudson River Gothic architecture of the middle Victorian period. Full, sound discussions of general aspects of housing, architecture, style, decoration, furnishing, together with scores of detailed house plans, illustrations of specific buildings, accompanied by full text. Perhaps the most influential single American architectural book. 1850 edition. Introduction by J. Stewart Johnson. 321 figures, 34 architectural designs. xvi + 560pp.
22003-6 Paperbound $4.00

LOST EXAMPLES OF COLONIAL ARCHITECTURE, John Mead Howells. Full-page photographs of buildings that have disappeared or been so altered as to be denatured, including many designed by major early American architects. 245 plates. xvii + 248pp. 7⅞ x 10¾.
21143-6 Paperbound $3.50

DOMESTIC ARCHITECTURE OF THE AMERICAN COLONIES AND OF THE EARLY REPUBLIC, Fiske Kimball. Foremost architect and restorer of Williamsburg and Monticello covers nearly 200 homes between 1620-1825. Architectural details, construction, style features, special fixtures, floor plans, etc. Generally considered finest work in its area. 219 illustrations of houses, doorways, windows, capital mantels. xx + 314pp. 7⅞ x 10¾.
21743-4 Paperbound $4.00

EARLY AMERICAN ROOMS: 1650-1858, edited by Russell Hawes Kettell. Tour of 12 rooms, each representative of a different era in American history and each furnished, decorated, designed and occupied in the style of the era. 72 plans and elevations, 8-page color section, etc., show fabrics, wall papers, arrangements, etc. Full descriptive text. xvii + 200pp. of text. 8⅜ x 11¼.
21633-0 Paperbound $5.00

THE FITZWILLIAM VIRGINAL BOOK, edited by J. Fuller Maitland and W. B. Squire. Full modern printing of famous early 17th-century ms. volume of 300 works by Morley, Byrd, Bull, Gibbons, etc. For piano or other modern keyboard instrument; easy to read format. xxxvi + 938pp. 8⅜ x 11.
21068-5, 21069-3 Two volumes, Paperbound $10.00

KEYBOARD MUSIC, Johann Sebastian Bach. Bach Gesellschaft edition. A rich selection of Bach's masterpieces for the harpsichord: the six English Suites, six French Suites, the six Partitas (Clavierübung part I), the Goldberg Variations (Clavierübung part IV), the fifteen Two-Part Inventions and the fifteen Three-Part Sinfonias. Clearly reproduced on large sheets with ample margins; eminently playable. vi + 312pp. 8⅛ x 11.
22360-4 Paperbound $5.00

THE MUSIC OF BACH: AN INTRODUCTION, Charles Sanford Terry. A fine, nontechnical introduction to Bach's music, both instrumental and vocal. Covers organ music, chamber music, passion music, other types. Analyzes themes, developments, innovations. x + 114pp.
21075-8 Paperbound $1.25

BEETHOVEN AND HIS NINE SYMPHONIES, Sir George Grove. Noted British musicologist provides best history, analysis, commentary on symphonies. Very thorough, rigorously accurate; necessary to both advanced student and amateur music lover. 436 musical passages. vii + 407 pp.
20334-4 Paperbound $2.75

JOHANN SEBASTIAN BACH, Philipp Spitta. One of the great classics of musicology, this definitive analysis of Bach's music (and life) has never been surpassed. Lucid, nontechnical analyses of hundreds of pieces (30 pages devoted to St. Matthew Passion, 26 to B Minor Mass). Also includes major analysis of 18th-century music. 450 musical examples. 40-page musical supplement. Total of xx + 1799pp.

(EUK) 22278-0, 22279-9 Two volumes, Clothbound $17.50

MOZART AND HIS PIANO CONCERTOS, Cuthbert Girdlestone. The only full-length study of an important area of Mozart's creativity. Provides detailed analyses of all 23 concertos, traces inspirational sources. 417 musical examples. Second edition. 509pp.
21271-8 Paperbound $3.50

THE PERFECT WAGNERITE: A COMMENTARY ON THE NIBLUNG'S RING, George Bernard Shaw. Brilliant and still relevant criticism in remarkable essays on Wagner's Ring cycle, Shaw's ideas on political and social ideology behind the plots, role of Leitmotifs, vocal requisites, etc. Prefaces. xxi + 136pp.

(USO) 21707-8 Paperbound $1.50

DON GIOVANNI, W. A. Mozart. Complete libretto, modern English translation; biographies of composer and librettist; accounts of early performances and critical reaction. Lavishly illustrated. All the material you need to understand and appreciate this great work. Dover Opera Guide and Libretto Series; translated and introduced by Ellen Bleiler. 92 illustrations. 209pp.

21134-7 Paperbound $2.00

HIGH FIDELITY SYSTEMS: A LAYMAN'S GUIDE, Roy F. Allison. All the basic information you need for setting up your own audio system: high fidelity and stereo record players, tape records, F.M. Connections, adjusting tone arm, cartridge, checking needle alignment, positioning speakers, phasing speakers, adjusting hums, trouble-shooting, maintenance, and similar topics. Enlarged 1965 edition. More than 50 charts, diagrams, photos. iv + 91pp. 21514-8 Paperbound $1.25

REPRODUCTION OF SOUND, Edgar Villchur. Thorough coverage for laymen of high fidelity systems, reproducing systems in general, needles, amplifiers, preamps, loudspeakers, feedback, explaining physical background. "A rare talent for making technicalities vividly comprehensible," R. Darrell, *High Fidelity*. 69 figures. iv + 92pp. 21515-6 Paperbound $1.25

HEAR ME TALKIN' TO YA: THE STORY OF JAZZ AS TOLD BY THE MEN WHO MADE IT, Nat Shapiro and Nat Hentoff. Louis Armstrong, Fats Waller, Jo Jones, Clarence Williams, Billy Holiday, Duke Ellington, Jelly Roll Morton and dozens of other jazz greats tell how it was in Chicago's South Side, New Orleans, depression Harlem and the modern West Coast as jazz was born and grew. xvi + 429pp.

21726-4 Paperbound $2.50

FABLES OF AESOP, translated by Sir Roger L'Estrange. A reproduction of the very rare 1931 Paris edition; a selection of the most interesting fables, together with 50 imaginative drawings by Alexander Calder. v + 128pp. 6½x9¼.

21780-9 Paperbound $1.50

AGAINST THE GRAIN (A REBOURS), Joris K. Huysmans. Filled with weird images, evidences of a bizarre imagination, exotic experiments with hallucinatory drugs, rich tastes and smells and the diversions of its sybarite hero Duc Jean des Esseintes, this classic novel pushed 19th-century literary decadence to its limits. Full unabridged edition. Do not confuse this with abridged editions generally sold. Introduction by Havelock Ellis. xlix + 206pp.   22190-3 Paperbound $2.00

VARIORUM SHAKESPEARE: HAMLET. Edited by Horace H. Furness; a landmark of American scholarship. Exhaustive footnotes and appendices treat all doubtful words and phrases, as well as suggested critical emendations throughout the play's history. First volume contains editor's own text, collated with all Quartos and Folios. Second volume contains full first Quarto, translations of Shakespeare's sources (Belleforest, and Saxo Grammaticus), Der Bestrafte Brudermord, and many essays on critical and historical points of interest by major authorities of past and present. Includes details of staging and costuming over the years. By far the best edition available for serious students of Shakespeare. Total of xx + 905pp.
21004-9, 21005-7, 2 volumes, Paperbound $7.00

A LIFE OF WILLIAM SHAKESPEARE, Sir Sidney Lee. This is the standard life of Shakespeare, summarizing everything known about Shakespeare and his plays. Incredibly rich in material, broad in coverage, clear and judicious, it has served thousands as the best introduction to Shakespeare. 1931 edition. 9 plates. xxix + 792pp.   (USO) 21967-4 Paperbound $3.75

MASTERS OF THE DRAMA, John Gassner. Most comprehensive history of the drama in print, covering every tradition from Greeks to modern Europe and America, including India, Far East, etc. Covers more than 800 dramatists, 2000 plays, with biographical material, plot summaries, theatre history, criticism, etc. "Best of its kind in English," *New Republic*. 77 illustrations. xxii + 890pp.
20100-7 Clothbound $8.50

THE EVOLUTION OF THE ENGLISH LANGUAGE, George McKnight. The growth of English, from the 14th century to the present. Unusual, non-technical account presents basic information in very interesting form: sound shifts, change in grammar and syntax, vocabulary growth, similar topics. Abundantly illustrated with quotations. Formerly *Modern English in the Making*. xii + 590pp.
21932-1 Paperbound $3.50

AN ETYMOLOGICAL DICTIONARY OF MODERN ENGLISH, Ernest Weekley. Fullest, richest work of its sort, by foremost British lexicographer. Detailed word histories, including many colloquial and archaic words; extensive quotations. Do not confuse this with the Concise Etymological Dictionary, which is much abridged. Total of xxvii + 830pp. 6½ x 9¼.
21873-2, 21874-0 Two volumes, Paperbound $6.00

FLATLAND: A ROMANCE OF MANY DIMENSIONS, E. A. Abbott. Classic of science-fiction explores ramifications of life in a two-dimensional world, and what happens when a three-dimensional being intrudes. Amusing reading, but also useful as introduction to thought about hyperspace. Introduction by Banesh Hoffmann. 16 illustrations. xx + 103pp.   20001-9 Paperbound $1.00

POEMS OF ANNE BRADSTREET, edited with an introduction by Robert Hutchinson. A new selection of poems by America's first poet and perhaps the first significant woman poet in the English language. 48 poems display her development in works of considerable variety—love poems, domestic poems, religious meditations, formal elegies, "quaternions," etc. Notes, bibliography. viii + 222pp.

22160-1 Paperbound $2.50

THREE GOTHIC NOVELS: THE CASTLE OF OTRANTO BY HORACE WALPOLE; VATHEK BY WILLIAM BECKFORD; THE VAMPYRE BY JOHN POLIDORI, WITH FRAGMENT OF A NOVEL BY LORD BYRON, edited by E. F. Bleiler. The first Gothic novel, by Walpole; the finest Oriental tale in English, by Beckford; powerful Romantic supernatural story in versions by Polidori and Byron. All extremely important in history of literature; all still exciting, packed with supernatural thrills, ghosts, haunted castles, magic, etc. xl + 291pp.

21232-7 Paperbound $2.50

THE BEST TALES OF HOFFMANN, E. T. A. Hoffmann. 10 of Hoffmann's most important stories, in modern re-editings of standard translations: Nutcracker and the King of Mice, Signor Formica, Automata, The Sandman, Rath Krespel, The Golden Flowerpot, Master Martin the Cooper, The Mines of Falun, The King's Betrothed, A New Year's Eve Adventure. 7 illustrations by Hoffmann. Edited by E. F. Bleiler. xxxix + 419pp. 21793-0 Paperbound $3.00

GHOST AND HORROR STORIES OF AMBROSE BIERCE, Ambrose Bierce. 23 strikingly modern stories of the horrors latent in the human mind: The Eyes of the Panther, The Damned Thing, An Occurrence at Owl Creek Bridge, An Inhabitant of Carcosa, etc., plus the dream-essay, Visions of the Night. Edited by E. F. Bleiler. xxii + 199pp. 20767-6 Paperbound $1.50

BEST GHOST STORIES OF J. S. LEFANU, J. Sheridan LeFanu. Finest stories by Victorian master often considered greatest supernatural writer of all. Carmilla, Green Tea, The Haunted Baronet, The Familiar, and 12 others. Most never before available in the U. S. A. Edited by E. F. Bleiler. 8 illustrations from Victorian publications. xvii + 467pp. 20415-4 Paperbound $3.00

MATHEMATICAL FOUNDATIONS OF INFORMATION THEORY, A. I. Khinchin. Comprehensive introduction to work of Shannon, McMillan, Feinstein and Khinchin, placing these investigations on a rigorous mathematical basis. Covers entropy concept in probability theory, uniqueness theorem, Shannon's inequality, ergodic sources, the E property, martingale concept, noise, Feinstein's fundamental lemma, Shanon's first and second theorems. Translated by R. A. Silverman and M. D. Friedman. iii + 120pp. 60434-9 Paperbound $1.75

SEVEN SCIENCE FICTION NOVELS, H. G. Wells. The standard collection of the great novels. Complete, unabridged. *First Men in the Moon, Island of Dr. Moreau, War of the Worlds, Food of the Gods, Invisible Man, Time Machine, In the Days of the Comet.* Not only science fiction fans, but every educated person owes it to himself to read these novels. 1015pp. (USO) 20264-X Clothbound $5.00

LAST AND FIRST MEN AND STAR MAKER, TWO SCIENCE FICTION NOVELS, Olaf Stapledon. Greatest future histories in science fiction. In the first, human intelligence is the "hero," through strange paths of evolution, interplanetary invasions, incredible technologies, near extinctions and reemergences. Star Maker describes the quest of a band of star rovers for intelligence itself, through time and space: weird inhuman civilizations, crustacean minds, symbiotic worlds, etc. Complete, unabridged. v + 438pp. (USO) 21962-3 Paperbound $2.50

THREE PROPHETIC NOVELS, H. G. WELLS. Stages of a consistently planned future for mankind. *When the Sleeper Wakes,* and *A Story of the Days to Come,* anticipate *Brave New World* and *1984,* in the 21st Century; *The Time Machine,* only complete version in print, shows farther future and the end of mankind. All show Wells's greatest gifts as storyteller and novelist. Edited by E. F. Bleiler. x + 335pp. (USO) 20605-X Paperbound $2.50

THE DEVIL'S DICTIONARY, Ambrose Bierce. America's own Oscar Wilde—Ambrose Bierce—offers his barbed iconoclastic wisdom in over 1,000 definitions hailed by H. L. Mencken as "some of the most gorgeous witticisms in the English language." 145pp. 20487-1 Paperbound $1.25

MAX AND MORITZ, Wilhelm Busch. Great children's classic, father of comic strip, of two bad boys, Max and Moritz. Also Ker and Plunk (Plisch und Plumm), Cat and Mouse, Deceitful Henry, Ice-Peter, The Boy and the Pipe, and five other pieces. Original German, with English translation. Edited by H. Arthur Klein; translations by various hands and H. Arthur Klein. vi + 216pp. 20181-3 Paperbound $2.00

PIGS IS PIGS AND OTHER FAVORITES, Ellis Parker Butler. The title story is one of the best humor short stories, as Mike Flannery obfuscates biology and English. Also included, That Pup of Murchison's, The Great American Pie Company, and Perkins of Portland. 14 illustrations. v + 109pp. 21532-6 Paperbound $1.25

THE PETERKIN PAPERS, Lucretia P. Hale. It takes genius to be as stupidly mad as the Peterkins, as they decide to become wise, celebrate the "Fourth," keep a cow, and otherwise strain the resources of the Lady from Philadelphia. Basic book of American humor. 153 illustrations. 219pp. 20794-3 Paperbound $1.50

PERRAULT'S FAIRY TALES, translated by A. E. Johnson and S. R. Littlewood, with 34 full-page illustrations by Gustave Doré. All the original Perrault stories—Cinderella, Sleeping Beauty, Bluebeard, Little Red Riding Hood, Puss in Boots, Tom Thumb, etc.—with their witty verse morals and the magnificent illustrations of Doré. One of the five or six great books of European fairy tales. viii + 117pp. 8⅛ x 11. 22311-6 Paperbound $2.00

OLD HUNGARIAN FAIRY TALES, Baroness Orczy. Favorites translated and adapted by author of the *Scarlet Pimpernel.* Eight fairy tales include "The Suitors of Princess Fire-Fly," "The Twin Hunchbacks," "Mr. Cuttlefish's Love Story," and "The Enchanted Cat." This little volume of magic and adventure will captivate children as it has for generations. 90 drawings by Montagu Barstow. 96pp. 22293-4 Paperbound $1.95

THE RED FAIRY BOOK, Andrew Lang. Lang's color fairy books have long been children's favorites. This volume includes Rapunzel, Jack and the Bean-stalk and 35 other stories, familiar and unfamiliar. 4 plates, 93 illustrations x + 367pp.
21673-X Paperbound $2.50

THE BLUE FAIRY BOOK, Andrew Lang. Lang's tales come from all countries and all times. Here are 37 tales from Grimm, the Arabian Nights, Greek Mythology, and other fascinating sources. 8 plates, 130 illustrations. xi + 390pp.
21437-0 Paperbound $2.50

HOUSEHOLD STORIES BY THE BROTHERS GRIMM. Classic English-language edition of the well-known tales — Rumpelstiltskin, Snow White, Hansel and Gretel, The Twelve Brothers, Faithful John, Rapunzel, Tom Thumb (52 stories in all). Translated into simple, straightforward English by Lucy Crane. Ornamented with headpieces, vignettes, elaborate decorative initials and a dozen full-page illustrations by Walter Crane. x + 269pp.
21080-4 Paperbound $2.00

THE MERRY ADVENTURES OF ROBIN HOOD, Howard Pyle. The finest modern versions of the traditional ballads and tales about the great English outlaw. Howard Pyle's complete prose version, with every word, every illustration of the first edition. Do not confuse this facsimile of the original (1883) with modern editions that change text or illustrations. 23 plates plus many page decorations. xxii + 296pp.
22043-5 Paperbound $2.50

THE STORY OF KING ARTHUR AND HIS KNIGHTS, Howard Pyle. The finest children's version of the life of King Arthur; brilliantly retold by Pyle, with 48 of his most imaginative illustrations. xviii + 313pp. 6⅛ x 9¼.
21445-1 Paperbound $2.50

THE WONDERFUL WIZARD OF OZ, L. Frank Baum. America's finest children's book in facsimile of first edition with all Denslow illustrations in full color. The edition a child should have. Introduction by Martin Gardner. 23 color plates, scores of drawings. iv + 267pp.
20691-2 Paperbound $2.50

THE MARVELOUS LAND OF OZ, L. Frank Baum. The second Oz book, every bit as imaginative as the Wizard. The hero is a boy named Tip, but the Scarecrow and the Tin Woodman are back, as is the Oz magic. 16 color plates, 120 drawings by John R. Neill. 287pp.
20692-0 Paperbound $2.50

THE MAGICAL MONARCH OF MO, L. Frank Baum. Remarkable adventures in a land even stranger than Oz. The best of Baum's books not in the Oz series. 15 color plates and dozens of drawings by Frank Verbeck. xviii + 237pp.
21892-9 Paperbound $2.25

THE BAD CHILD'S BOOK OF BEASTS, MORE BEASTS FOR WORSE CHILDREN, A MORAL ALPHABET, Hilaire Belloc. Three complete humor classics in one volume. Be kind to the frog, and do not call him names . . . and 28 other whimsical animals. Familiar favorites and some not so well known. Illustrated by Basil Blackwell. 156pp.
(USO) 20749-8 Paperbound $1.50

EAST O' THE SUN AND WEST O' THE MOON, George W. Dasent. Considered the best of all translations of these Norwegian folk tales, this collection has been enjoyed by generations of children (and folklorists too). Includes True and Untrue, Why the Sea is Salt, East O' the Sun and West O' the Moon, Why the Bear is Stumpy-Tailed, Boots and the Troll, The Cock and the Hen, Rich Peter the Pedlar, and 52 more. The only edition with all 59 tales. 77 illustrations by Erik Werenskiold and Theodor Kittelsen. xv + 418pp. 22521-6 Paperbound $3.50

GOOPS AND HOW TO BE THEM, Gelett Burgess. Classic of tongue-in-cheek humor, masquerading as etiquette book. 87 verses, twice as many cartoons, show mischievous Goops as they demonstrate to children virtues of table manners, neatness, courtesy, etc. Favorite for generations. viii + 88pp. $6\frac{1}{2}$ x $9\frac{1}{4}$. 22233-0 Paperbound $1.25

ALICE'S ADVENTURES UNDER GROUND, Lewis Carroll. The first version, quite different from the final *Alice in Wonderland,* printed out by Carroll himself with his own illustrations. Complete facsimile of the "million dollar" manuscript Carroll gave to Alice Liddell in 1864. Introduction by Martin Gardner. viii + 96pp. Title and dedication pages in color. 21482-6 Paperbound $1.25

THE BROWNIES, THEIR BOOK, Palmer Cox. Small as mice, cunning as foxes, exuberant and full of mischief, the Brownies go to the zoo, toy shop, seashore, circus, etc., in 24 verse adventures and 266 illustrations. Long a favorite, since their first appearance in St. Nicholas Magazine. xi + 144pp. $6\frac{5}{8}$ x $9\frac{1}{4}$. 21265-3 Paperbound $1.75

SONGS OF CHILDHOOD, Walter De La Mare. Published (under the pseudonym Walter Ramal) when De La Mare was only 29, this charming collection has long been a favorite children's book. A facsimile of the first edition in paper, the 47 poems capture the simplicity of the nursery rhyme and the ballad, including such lyrics as I Met Eve, Tartary, The Silver Penny. vii + 106pp. (USO) 21972-0 Paperbound $1.25

THE COMPLETE NONSENSE OF EDWARD LEAR, Edward Lear. The finest 19th-century humorist-cartoonist in full: all nonsense limericks, zany alphabets, Owl and Pussycat, songs, nonsense botany, and more than 500 illustrations by Lear himself. Edited by Holbrook Jackson. xxix + 287pp. (USO) 20167-8 Paperbound $2.00

BILLY WHISKERS: THE AUTOBIOGRAPHY OF A GOAT, Frances Trego Montgomery. A favorite of children since the early 20th century, here are the escapades of that rambunctious, irresistible and mischievous goat—Billy Whiskers. Much in the spirit of *Peck's Bad Boy,* this is a book that children never tire of reading or hearing. All the original familiar illustrations by W. H. Fry are included: 6 color plates, 18 black and white drawings. 159pp. 22345-0 Paperbound $2.00

MOTHER GOOSE MELODIES. Faithful republication of the fabulously rare Munroe and Francis "copyright 1833" Boston edition—the most important Mother Goose collection, usually referred to as the "original." Familiar rhymes plus many rare ones, with wonderful old woodcut illustrations. Edited by E. F. Bleiler. 128pp. $4\frac{1}{2}$ x $6\frac{3}{8}$. 22577-1 Paperbound $1.00

TWO LITTLE SAVAGES; BEING THE ADVENTURES OF TWO BOYS WHO LIVED AS INDIANS AND WHAT THEY LEARNED, Ernest Thompson Seton. Great classic of nature and boyhood provides a vast range of woodlore in most palatable form, a genuinely entertaining story. Two farm boys build a teepee in woods and live in it for a month, working out Indian solutions to living problems, star lore, birds and animals, plants, etc. 293 illustrations. vii + 286pp.

20985-7 Paperbound $2.50

PETER PIPER'S PRACTICAL PRINCIPLES OF PLAIN & PERFECT PRONUNCIATION. Alliterative jingles and tongue-twisters of surprising charm, that made their first appearance in America about 1830. Republished in full with the spirited woodcut illustrations from this earliest American edition. 32pp. $4\frac{1}{2}$ x $6\frac{3}{8}$.

22560-7 Paperbound $1.00

SCIENCE EXPERIMENTS AND AMUSEMENTS FOR CHILDREN, Charles Vivian. 73 easy experiments, requiring only materials found at home or easily available, such as candles, coins, steel wool, etc.; illustrate basic phenomena like vacuum, simple chemical reaction, etc. All safe. Modern, well-planned. Formerly *Science Games for Children*. 102 photos, numerous drawings. 96pp. $6\frac{1}{8}$ x $9\frac{1}{4}$.

21856-2 Paperbound $1.25

AN INTRODUCTION TO CHESS MOVES AND TACTICS SIMPLY EXPLAINED, Leonard Barden. Informal intermediate introduction, quite strong in explaining reasons for moves. Covers basic material, tactics, important openings, traps, positional play in middle game, end game. Attempts to isolate patterns and recurrent configurations. Formerly *Chess*. 58 figures. 102pp. (USO) 21210-6 Paperbound $1.25

LASKER'S MANUAL OF CHESS, Dr. Emanuel Lasker. Lasker was not only one of the five great World Champions, he was also one of the ablest expositors, theorists, and analysts. In many ways, his Manual, permeated with his philosophy of battle, filled with keen insights, is one of the greatest works ever written on chess. Filled with analyzed games by the great players. A single-volume library that will profit almost any chess player, beginner or master. 308 diagrams. xli X 349pp.

20640-8 Paperbound $2.75

THE MASTER BOOK OF MATHEMATICAL RECREATIONS, Fred Schuh. In opinion of many the finest work ever prepared on mathematical puzzles, stunts, recreations; exhaustively thorough explanations of mathematics involved, analysis of effects, citation of puzzles and games. Mathematics involved is elementary. Translated by F. Göbel. 194 figures. xxiv + 430pp. 22134-2 Paperbound $3.00

MATHEMATICS, MAGIC AND MYSTERY, Martin Gardner. Puzzle editor for Scientific American explains mathematics behind various mystifying tricks: card tricks, stage "mind reading," coin and match tricks, counting out games, geometric dissections, etc. Probability sets, theory of numbers clearly explained. Also provides more than 400 tricks, guaranteed to work, that you can do. 135 illustrations. xii + 176pp.

20335-2 Paperbound $1.50

MATHEMATICAL PUZZLES FOR BEGINNERS AND ENTHUSIASTS, Geoffrey Mott-Smith. 189 puzzles from easy to difficult—involving arithmetic, logic, algebra, properties of digits, probability, etc.—for enjoyment and mental stimulus. Explanation of mathematical principles behind the puzzles. 135 illustrations. viii + 248pp.
20198-8 Paperbound $1.75

PAPER FOLDING FOR BEGINNERS, William D. Murray and Francis J. Rigney. Easiest book on the market, clearest instructions on making interesting, beautiful origami. Sail boats, cups, roosters, frogs that move legs, bonbon boxes, standing birds, etc. 40 projects; more than 275 diagrams and photographs. 94pp.
20713-7 Paperbound $1.00

TRICKS AND GAMES ON THE POOL TABLE, Fred Herrmann. 79 tricks and games— some solitaires, some for two or more players, some competitive games—to entertain you between formal games. Mystifying shots and throws, unusual caroms, tricks involving such props as cork, coins, a hat, etc. Formerly *Fun on the Pool Table*. 77 figures. 95pp.
21814-7 Paperbound $1.00

HAND SHADOWS TO BE THROWN UPON THE WALL: A SERIES OF NOVEL AND AMUSING FIGURES FORMED BY THE HAND, Henry Bursill. Delightful picturebook from great-grandfather's day shows how to make 18 different hand shadows: a bird that flies, duck that quacks, dog that wags his tail, camel, goose, deer, boy, turtle, etc. Only book of its sort. vi + 33pp. 6½ x 9¼. 21779-5 Paperbound $1.00

WHITTLING AND WOODCARVING, E. J. Tangerman. 18th printing of best book on market. "If you can cut a potato you can carve" toys and puzzles, chains, chessmen, caricatures, masks, frames, woodcut blocks, surface patterns, much more. Information on tools, woods, techniques. Also goes into serious wood sculpture from Middle Ages to present, East and West. 464 photos, figures. x + 293pp.
20965-2 Paperbound $2.00

HISTORY OF PHILOSOPHY, Julián Marias. Possibly the clearest, most easily followed, best planned, most useful one-volume history of philosophy on the market; neither skimpy nor overfull. Full details on system of every major philosopher and dozens of less important thinkers from pre-Socratics up to Existentialism and later. Strong on many European figures usually omitted. Has gone through dozens of editions in Europe. 1966 edition, translated by Stanley Appelbaum and Clarence Strowbridge. xviii + 505pp. 21739-6 Paperbound $3.50

YOGA: A SCIENTIFIC EVALUATION, Kovoor T. Behanan. Scientific but non-technical study of physiological results of yoga exercises; done under auspices of Yale U. Relations to Indian thought, to psychoanalysis, etc. 16 photos. xxiii + 270pp.
20505-3 Paperbound $2.50

Prices subject to change without notice.
Available at your book dealer or write for free catalogue to Dept. GI, Dover Publications, Inc., 180 Varick St., N. Y., N. Y. 10014. Dover publishes more than 150 books each year on science, elementary and advanced mathematics, biology, music, art, literary history, social sciences and other areas.